SPELLING PLUS

Grade 1

SPELLING PLUS

Grade 1

Third Edition

purposeful design
p u b l i c a t i o n s

Colorado Springs, Colorado

Purposeful Design Publications is the publishing division of the Association of Christian Schools International (ACSI) and is committed to the ministry of Christian school education, to enable Christian educators and schools worldwide to effectively prepare students for life. As the publisher of textbooks, trade books, and other educational resources within ACSI, Purposeful Design Publications strives to produce biblically sound materials that reflect Christian scholarship and stewardship and that address the identified needs of Christian schools around the world.

References to books, computer software, and other ancillary resources in this series are not endorsements by ACSI Purposeful Design Publications. These materials were selected to provide teachers with additional resources appropriate to the concepts being taught and to promote student understanding and enjoyment.

Unless otherwise identified, all Scripture quotations are taken from the Holy Bible, New King James Version (NKJV), © 1982 by Thomas Nelson, Inc. Used by permission. All rights reserved.

Photo of the umbrella bird on Student Edition pages 63 and 186 courtesy of Larry Wan of the Western Alliance for Nature, www.wanconservancy.org. Used by permission.

Currency images on Student Edition pages 10, 20, and 40 courtesy of United States Mint.

Printed in the United Sates of America
25 24 23 22 21 20   2 3 4 5 6 7

Spelling Plus, Grade 1
Purposeful Design Spelling Plus series
ISBN 978-1-58331-307-7   Student Edition   Catalog #60011

Purposeful Design Publications
A Division of ACSI
731 Chapel Hills Drive • Colorado Springs, CO 80920
Customer Service: 800-367-0798 • Website: www.purposefuldesign.org

Table of Contents

Listen to the story that the teacher reads.

beagle

Trace and write each letter.

1. B B

2. b b

Circle the letter that stands for the beginning sound.

3.

_ear

m   t

b   p

Write the letter **b** if the picture word begins like **beagle**.

1. _____   2. _____   3. _____   4. _____

Write the beginning letter to complete each word.

5. _____at   6. _____oat   7. _____ow

Write a capital **B** at the beginning of each name.

8. _____en   9. _____ingo

2

Name _____

Listen to the story that the teacher reads.

monkeys

Trace and write each letter.

1.

2.

Circle the letter that stands for the beginning sound.

3.

_ouse

m   t

b   c

Write the letter **m** if the picture word begins like  **monkey**.

1. _____   2. _____   3. _____   4. _____

Write the beginning letter to complete each word.

5. _____ ap   6. _____ an   7. _____ ilk

Write a capital **M** at the beginning of each name.

8. _____ in   9. _____ ax

4

Listen to the story that the teacher reads.

tortoise

Trace and write each letter.

1. _____   2. _____

Circle the letter that stands for the beginning sound.

3.

_iger

m   t

b   c

Write the letter **t** if the picture word begins like **tortoise**.

1. _____ 2. _____ 3. _____ 4. _____

Write the beginning letter to complete each word.

5. ___ent   6. ___ie   7. ___ape

Write a capital **T** at the beginning of each name.

8. ___ara   9. ___ed

6

Name _____

1.4 b, m, t, Cc, p

Listen to the story that the teacher reads.

cardinal

Trace and write each letter.

1. C C C _____

2. c c _____

Circle the letter that stands for the beginning sound.

3.

_entipede

m   b

t   c

Write the letter **c** if the picture word begins like **cardinal**.

1. _____
2. _____
3. _____
4. _____

Write the letter **c** if the picture word begins like **circle**.

5. _____
6. _____
7. _____
8. _____

Write a capital **C** at the beginning of each name.

9. _____arlos
10. _____elina
11. _____asey

8

Name _____

Listen to the story that the teacher reads.

penguins

Trace and write each letter.

1. P P

2. p p

Circle the letter that stands for the beginning sound.

3.

_anda

m   t

p   c

Write the letter **p** if the picture word begins like **penguin**.

1. _____
2. _____
3. _____
4. _____

Write the beginning letter to complete each word.

5. ____ig
6. ____in
7. ____enny

Write a capital **P** at the beginning of each name.

8. ____awan
9. ____eep

10

Listen to the story that the teacher reads.

lamb

Trace and write each letter.

1.    2.

Circle the letter that stands for the beginning sound.

3.

_ion

s   p
l   b

Write the letter **l** if the picture word begins like 🐑 **lamb**.

1. _____   2. _____   3. _____   4. _____

Write the beginning letter to complete each word.

5. ___eaf   6. ___ips   7. ___emon

Write a capital **L** at the beginning of each name.

8. ___ucy   9. ___ily   10. ___ester

Listen to the story that the teacher reads.

newt

Trace and write each letter.

1. N N

2. n n

Circle the letter that stands for the beginning sound.

3.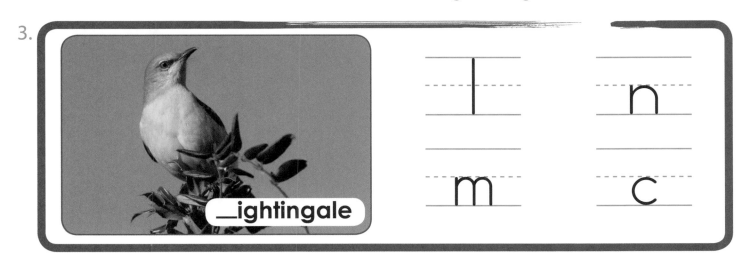

_ightingale

l   n

m   c

Write the letter **n** if the picture word begins like  **newt**.

1. _____

2. _____

3. _____

4. _____

Write the beginning letter to complete each word.

5. _____urse

6. _____ine

7. _____ose

Write a capital **N** at the beginning of each name.

8. _____ate

9. _____eon

Listen to the story that the teacher reads.

rabbit

Trace and write each letter.

1. R R R

2. r r r

Circle the letter that stands for the beginning sound.

3.

_hinoceros

r   n

l   b

Write the letter **r** if the picture word begins like  **rabbit**.

1. _____ 2. _____ 3. _____ 4. _____

Write the beginning letter to complete each word.

5. ___ose 6. ___aft 7. ___ibbon

Write a capital **R** at the beginning of each name.

8. ___aylin 9. ___ay

16

Name _____

Listen to the story that the teacher reads.

guinea pig

Trace and write each letter.

1. G G _____

2. g g _____

Circle the letter that stands for the beginning sound.

3.

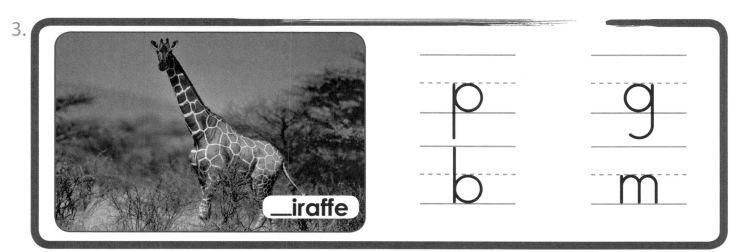

_iraffe

p   g

b   m

Write the letter **g** if the picture word begins like **guinea pig**.

1. _____

2. _____

3. _____

4. _____

Write the letter **g** if the picture word begins like **giraffe**.

5. _____

6. _____

7. _____

8. _____

Write a capital **G** at the beginning of each name.

9. ____inger

10. ____izmo

18

Listen to the story that the teacher reads.

dolphins

Trace and write each letter.

1. D D

2. d d

Circle the letter that stands for the beginning sound.

3.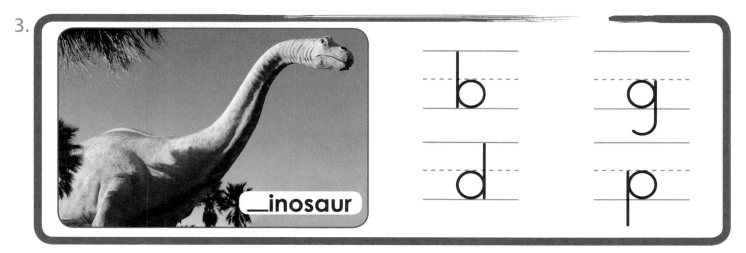

_inosaur

b

d

g

p

Write the letter **d** if the picture word begins like **dolphin**.

1. _____ 2. _____ 3. _____ 4. _____

Write the beginning letter to complete each word.

5. _esk 6. _ollar 7. _oor

Write a capital **D** at the beginning of each name.

8. _iego 9. _ip

Listen to the story that the teacher reads.

seal

Trace and write each letter.

1. S S _____

2. s s _____

Circle the letter that stands for the beginning sound.

3.

_almon

r   b

c   s

Write the letter **s** if the picture word begins like  **seal**.

1. _____   2. _____   3. _____   4. _____

Write the beginning letter to complete each word.

5. _alad   6. _oap   7. _aw

Write a capital **S** at the beginning of each name.

8. _ue   9. _am

22

Name _____

Listen to the story that the teacher reads.

fish

Trace and write each letter.

1. F F   f f
2.

Circle the letter that stands for the beginning sound.

3.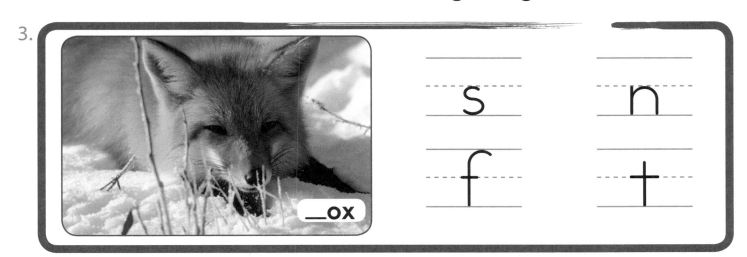

_ox

s   n

f   t

Write the letter **f** if the picture word begins like **fish**.

1. _____   2. _____   3. _____   4. _____

Write the beginning letter to complete each word.

5. ___ive   6. ___arm   7. ___ace

Write a capital **F** at the beginning of each name.

8. ___aye   9. ___elix

Listen to the story that the teacher reads.

horses

Trace and write each letter.

1. H H

2. h h

Circle the letter that stands for the beginning sound.

3.

_ummingbird

g
h

l
m

Write the letter **h** if the picture word begins like **horse**.

1. _____

2. _____

3. _____

4. _____

Write the beginning letter to complete each word.

5. ___ and

6. ___ ose

7. ___ at

Write a capital **H** at the beginning of each name.

8. ___ ailey

9. ___ ero

26

Name _____

Listen to the story that the teacher reads.

jaguar

Trace and write each letter.

1. J J _____

2. j j _____

Circle the letter that stands for the beginning sound.

3.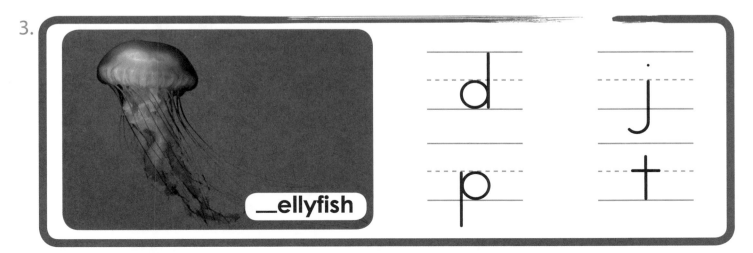
_ellyfish

d
p

j
t

Write the letter **j** if the picture word begins like  **jaguar**.

1. _____

2. _____

3. _____

4. _____

Write the beginning letter to complete each word.

5. ___et

6. ___uice

7. ___acks

Write a capital **J** at the beginning of each name.

8. ___in

9. ___ungle

28

Name _____

Listen to the story that the teacher reads.

walrus

Trace and write each letter.

1. W W _____   2. W W _____

Circle the letter that stands for the beginning sound.

3.

_olf

m   c

w   f

Write the letter **w** if the picture word begins like 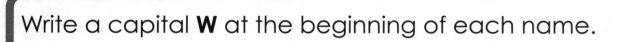 **walrus**.

1. _____

2. _____

3. _____

4. _____

Write the beginning letter to complete each word.

5. ___eb

6. ___orm

7. ___asp

Write a capital **W** at the beginning of each name.

8. ___ade

9. ___illy

Name _____

Listen to the story that the teacher reads.

kangaroo

Trace and write each letter.

1. K K K

2. k k k

Circle the letter that stands for the beginning sound.

3.

_oala

m   s

k   r

Write the letter **k** if the picture word begins like  **kangaroo**.

1. _____

2. _____

3. _____

4. _____

Write the beginning letter to complete each word.

5. ___ite

6. ___ey

7. ___ing

Write a capital **K** at the beginning of each name.

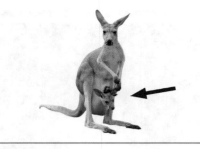

8. ___aji

9. ___ip

32

Name _____

Listen to the story that the teacher reads.

vicuña

Trace and write each letter.

1. V V

2. V V

Circle the letter that stands for the beginning sound.

3.

_ulture

m   v

f   c

Write the letter **v** if the picture word begins like 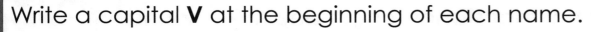 **vicuña**.

1. _____   2. _____   3. _____   4. _____

Write the beginning letter to complete each word.

5. _____ine   6. _____an   7. _____est

Write a capital **V** at the beginning of each name.

8. _____incent   9. _____ic

34

Listen to the story that the teacher reads.

yak

Trace and write each letter.

1. Y Y _____

2. y y _____

Circle the letter that stands for the beginning sound.

3.

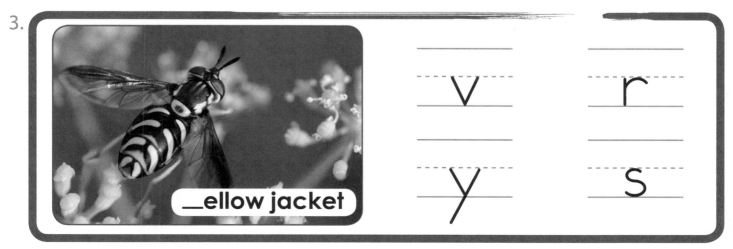

_ellow jacket

v   r

y   s

Write the letter **y** if the picture word begins like **yak**.

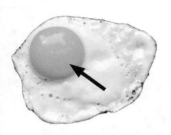   

1. _____ 2. _____ 3. _____ 4. _____

Write the beginning letter to complete each word.

5. _____arn 6. _____ellow 7. _____ogurt

Write a capital **Y** at the beginning of each name.

8. _____ana 9. _____oyo

36

Name _____

Listen to the story that the teacher reads.

zebras

Trace and write each letter.

1. Z Z _____   2. z z _____

Circle the letter that stands for the beginning sound.

3.
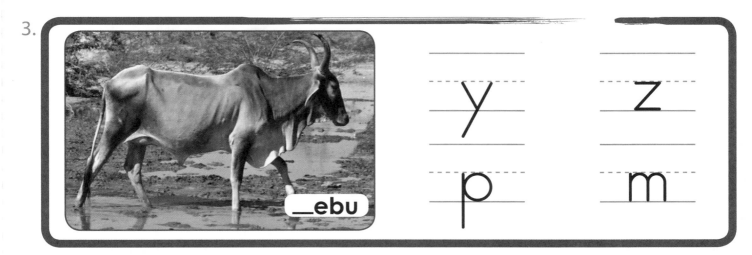

_ebu

y   z

p   m

Write the letter **z** if the picture word begins like zebra.

1. _____

2. _____

3. _____

4. _____

Write the beginning letter to complete each word.

5. ___igzag

6. ___ipper

7. ___ither

Write a capital **Z** at the beginning of each name.

8. ___ack

9. ___ora

38

Name _____

Listen to the story that the teacher reads.

quail

Trace and write each letter.

1. $Qu\ Qu$ _____

2. $qu\ qu$ _____

Circle the letter that stands for the beginning sound.

3.

___een bee

y   w

z   qu

Write the letter **qu** if the picture word begins like  **quail**.

1. _____

2. _____

3. _____

4. _____

Write the beginning letter to complete each word.

5. _____een

6. _____ilt

7. _____arter

Write **Qu** at the beginning of each name.

8. _____inn

9. _____at

40

Name _____

Listen to the story that the teacher reads.

fox

Trace and write each letter.

1. X X _____   2. X X _____

Circle the letter that stands for the ending sound.

3.

o__

x   m

g   r

Write the letter **x** if the picture word ends like **fox**.

1. _____   2. _____   3. _____   4. _____

Write the ending letter to complete each word.

5. wa_____   6. bo_____   7. fi_____

Write a lowercase **x** at the end of each name.

8. Ma_____   9. Re_____

42

Name each picture. Listen to each ending sound.
Write **b**, **m**, **t**, **p**, **n**, or **r** for the ending sound.

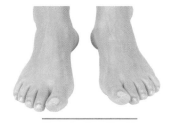

1. _____

2. _____

3. _____

4. _____

5. _____

6. _____

7. _____

8. _____

9. _____

10. _____

11. _____

12. _____

Name each picture. Circle the ending sound.

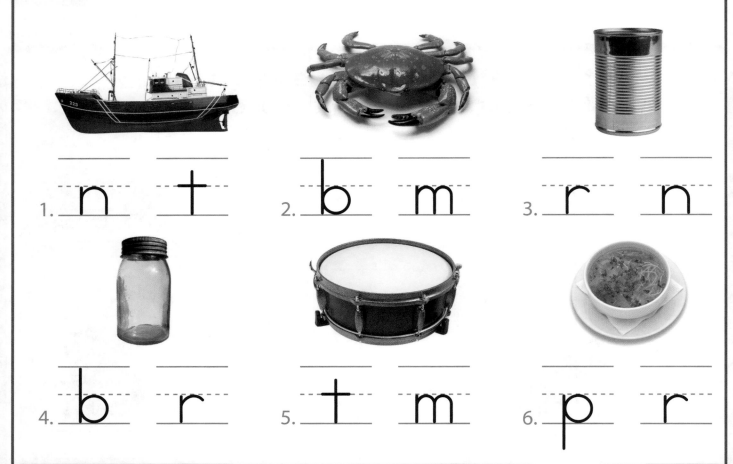

1. n   t

2. b   m

3. r   n

4. b   r

5. t   m

6. p   r

Name each picture. Circle two pictures in each row that end with the same sound.

7.

8.

44

Say each picture word. Draw a line from the picture
to the letter that makes the ending sound.

1.  •

                                                   •d

2.  •

                                                   •l

3.  •

                                                   •g

4.  •

                                                   •k

5.  •

                                                   •s

6.  •

                                                   •f

Say each picture word. Listen to the ending sound.
Write **d**, **l**, **g**, **k**, **s**, or **f** for the ending sound.

1. _____

2. _____

3. _____

4. _____

5. _____

6. _____

7. _____

8. _____

9. _____

10. _____

11. _____

12. _____

Help the squirrel collect acorns. Draw a line to connect each acorn in ABC order.

1.

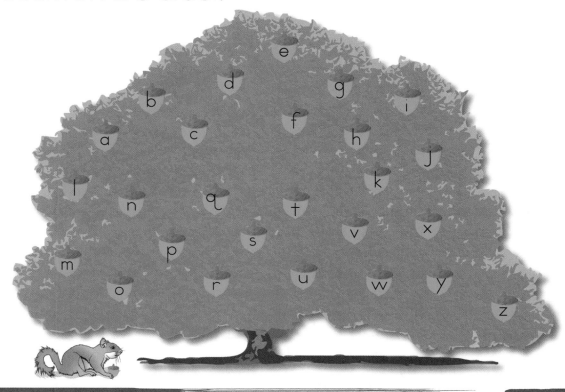

a b c d e f g h i j k l m n o p q r s t u v w x y z

Write the missing letters in each group, using ABC order.

2. a _____ c _____ e

3. v _____ y z

4. _____ n o p

Write the missing letters in each row.

1. _____ _____ _____ c _____
2. _____ _____ _____ m _____
3. j _____ _____ _____ _____
4. _____ _____ _____ _____ i
5. o _____ _____ _____ _____
6. _____ w _____ _____ _____
7. _____ _____ _____ v _____
8. _____ e _____ _____ _____

a b c d e f g h i j k l m n o p q r s t u v w x y z

Write the letter that comes before or after each letter.

9. _____ s _____
10. _____ j _____
11. _____ y _____
12. _____ w _____
13. _____ p _____
14. _____ t _____
15. _____ f _____
16. _____ n _____

A Spelling Study Strategy

1

- Look at the word.
- Say the word.
- Trace and say each letter.

2

- Think about how each sound is spelled.
- Picture the word in your mind.
- Write the word.

3

- Check your spelling.
- Does your spelling match the correct spelling?

- Look at the word.
- Say the word.
- Trace and say each letter.

- Think about the sounds.
- Picture the word.
- Write the word.
- Check your spelling.

Fold

1. am
2. at
3. can
4. man
5. ran
6. had
7. has
8. I
9. the
10.
11.
12.

1.
2.
3.
4.
5.
6.
7.
8.
9.
10.
11.
12.

Pattern Words

am

at

cat

can

man

ran

had

has

Trace and write each letter.

1. A A

ant

2. a a

> A vowel usually makes its short sound when it is the only vowel in the word.

Write the missing letters. Read the words.

3. ___ a ___

4. ___ a ___

5. ___ a ___

High-Frequency Words

I

the

Challenge Words

_____   _____

Sort the words by sound. Write the words that rhyme with each picture word.

Phonics
Short a

1. Rhymes with

_____
- - - - - - - - - - - - - - - - -
_____
- - - - - - - - - - - - - - - - -
_____

2. Rhymes with

_____
- - - - - - - - - - - - - - - - - - -
_____
- - - - - - - - - - - - - - - - - - -
_____
- - - - - - - - - - - - - - - - - - -
_____

am
at
cat
can
man
ran
had
has
I
the

3. Rhymes with

_____
- - - - - - - - - - - - - - - - -
_____

4. Rhymes with

_____
- - - - - - - - - - - - - - - - -
_____

5. Words that <u>do not have</u> the **short a** sound.

_____
- - - - - - - - - - - - - - -
_____
- - - - - - - - - - - - - - -
_____

52

am
at
cat
can
man
ran
had
has
I
the

Write the word that fits each sentence.

1. I _____ six years old.

2. James is _____  school.

3. The dog _____ in the park.

4. Emily _____ a new Bible.

5. Yesterday he _____ fun at the zoo.

6. Abby's pet _____ drinks milk.

7. That _____ had pizza for lunch.

Draw a line to match the correct meaning of **can** to the picture word.

8. knows how to do something •

•

9. a round, metal container •

•

Think of a cat. What words come to your mind?
Write them on the word web.

whisker

sleep cat tail

am
at
cat
can
man
ran
had
has
I
the

Write the missing words to complete the story.
Use the word web and the list.

_____

Abby talked to a _____ at the pet shop.

He showed Abby a white _____.

It _____ a fluffy _____. Abby liked

it and took it home. It _____ to its new bed.
Abby cared for her pet every day.

Give Abby's cat a name.
Write it on the tag.

_____

Pattern Words

job
God
mom
hop
top
got
not
fox

High-Frequency Words

a
and

Trace and write each letter.

1.

2.

otter

A vowel usually makes its short sound when it is the only vowel in the word.

Write the missing letters.

3. ___ o

4. ___ o

5. ___ o

6. ___ o

Challenge Words

_____ _____

Sort the words by the ending.
Write the words.

job
God
mom
hop
top
got
not
fox
a
and

1.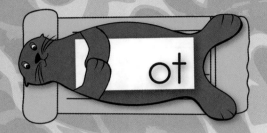

2.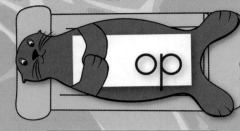

3.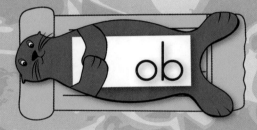

4.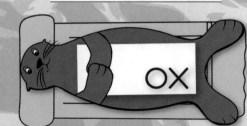

5.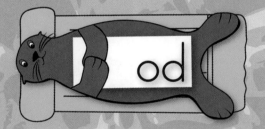

6.

Write the High-Frequency Words.

7. _____

8. _____

Name _____

Write the word that fits each sentence.

job
God
mom
hop
top
got
not
fox
a
and

1. My _____ gave me a cake.

_____

2. The cake had six | | | | | | candles on _____.

3. I did _____ cut the cake.

4. Mom _____ a 🔪 knife to cut it for me.

5.  I thanked _____ for the cake.

Draw a line to match each picture of **top** with its meaning.

6.

•   • the lid or cover

7.

•   • a toy that spins

8.

•   • the highest place

Write a note. Use the list words and some of your own words.

I will write a note to _____.

job
God
mom
hop
top
got
not
fox
a
and

Dear _____,

How are you? I am fine.

I _____ a good grade on my spelling test.

My teacher put _____ star on _____. I did a good _____.

Love,

_____

58

Pattern Words

bed

fed

red

get

let

pet

men

yes

Trace and write each letter.

1. E   E

2. e   e

A vowel usually makes its short sound when it is the only vowel in the word.

elephant

Write the missing vowel to make two words.

3.

m

y   ☐   s

n

Write the two words found in the puzzle above.

4. _____

5. _____

High-Frequency Words

for

as

Challenge Words

Sort the words by sound. Write the words on each elephant.

bed
fed
red
get
let
pet
men
yes
for
as

ed

1.

et

2.

Write the High-Frequency Words.

3.

4.

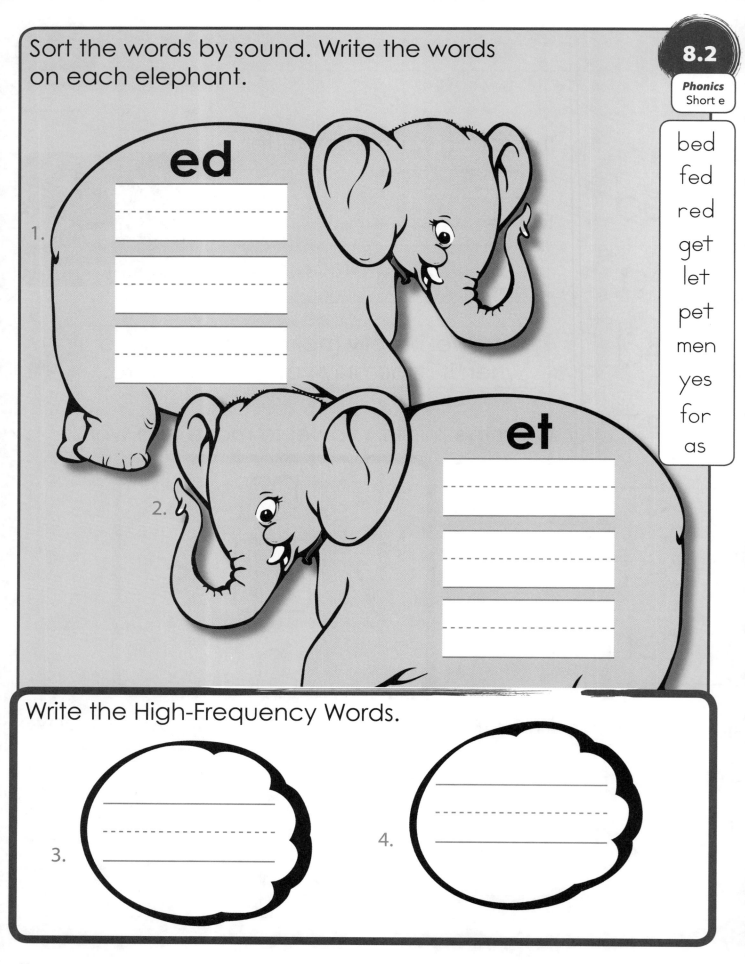

Name _____

Write the word that fits each sentence.

bed
fed
red
get
let
pet
men
yes
for
as

1. I go to _____ at 8:00 PM.

2. Ben has a _____ dog.

3. Mom will _____ us go to the beach.

4. The opposite of **no** is _____ .

5. The _____ played baseball.

6. Jen _____ a carrot to the bunny.

Circle the word that completes each sentence.

7. Ken has a _____ backpack.
    red   fed

8. Julie will _____ a book from the library.
    let   get

9. The birthday present is _____ Beth.
    as   for

Look at the book. Write the answers.

My Pet

Written and Illustrated by **Ben Zet**

What is the title?

_____

- - - - - - - - - - - - - - - - - - -

_____

Who is the author and illustrator?

_____

- - - - - - - - - - - - - - - - - - -

_____

bed
fed
red
get
let
pet
men
yes
for
as

Pretend you are an author and illustrator. Write a title using the word **red**. Draw a picture.

Written and Illustrated by

_____

- - - - - - - - - - - - - - - - - - -

_____

Pattern Words

up

us

mud

bug

fun

run

sun

cut

Trace and write each letter.

1. U U _____

umbrella bird

2. u u _____

A vowel usually makes its short sound when it is the only vowel in the word.

Look at each picture and read the words. Circle the correct word and write it.

3. bug
box
bed _____

4. men
mom
mud _____

5. cat
cut
can _____

High-Frequency Words

to

are

Challenge Words

_____   _____

Use the letters on the raindrops to make **un** words.

1.

up
us
mud
bug
fun
run
sun
cut
to
are

_____
\-\-\-\-\-\-\-\-\-\-\-\-\-\-
_____
\-\-\-\-\-\-\-\-\-\-\-\-\-\-
_____
\-\-\-\-\-\-\-\-\-\-\-\-\-\-
_____

Change each **a** to **u**. Write the new word.

2. as _____

3. cat _____

4. mad _____

5. bag _____

Write the words that begin like 🐦 umbrella bird.

6. _____

7. _____

Write the word that rhymes with rug.

8. _____

Write the words that do not have the **short u** sound.

9. _____

10. _____

64

Write the word that matches each meaning.

1. This is another name for an insect.

_____

2. You do this when your legs move quickly.

_____

3. It gives us heat and light.

_____

4. This word means to have a good time.

_____

up
us
mud
bug
fun
run
sun
cut
to
are

Write the missing word.

5. We _____ going to the zoo.

6. The balloon floated _____ into the sky.

7. Johnny went _____ the store.

8. Allie played in the _____ .

9. God loves _____ all.

He shall cover you with His feathers,
And under His wings you shall take refuge.
Psalm 91:4a

What does mud look like? How does it feel?
Write your answers on the word web.

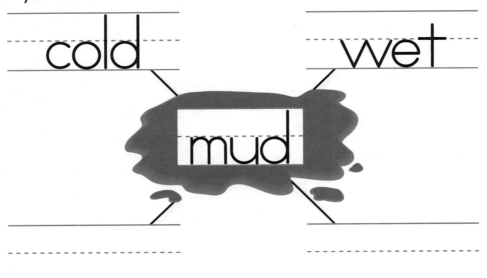

cold   wet

mud

up
us
mud
bug
fun
run
sun
cut
to
are

Write the missing words to complete the story.
Use the word web and the list.

Fun in the Mud

It is raining today. The [   ] hides

behind the clouds. When it comes out, we go outside

[   ] play and [   ] around.

The rain makes the dirt turn into [   ].

The mud feels [   ] and [   ].

It is a very [   ] day!

66

Name _____

Pattern Words

in

is

it

did

big

him

rip

fix

High-Frequency Words

was

of

Trace and write each letter.

1. I I

2. i i

iguana

A vowel usually makes its short sound when it is the only vowel in the word.

Circle each middle sound.
Write each missing letter.

3. a e i

b   g

4. a e i

r   p

Challenge Words

_____   _____

Write three words that begin like 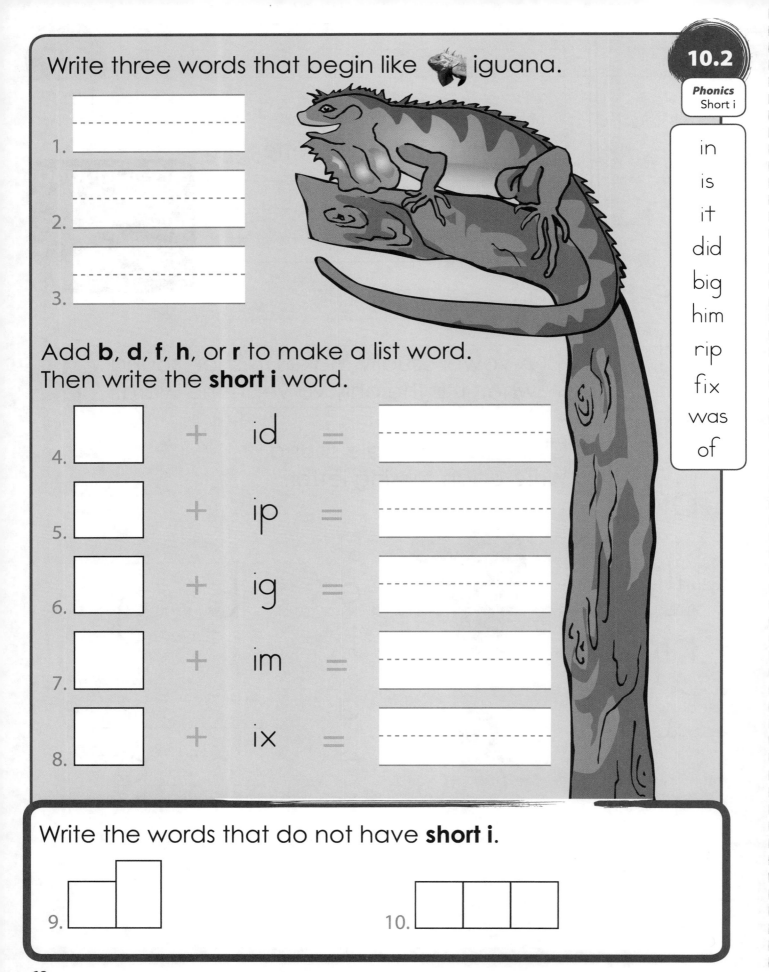 iguana.

1. _____

2. _____

3. _____

Add **b**, **d**, **f**, **h**, or **r** to make a list word.
Then write the **short i** word.

4. [ ] + id = _____

5. [ ] + ip = _____

6. [ ] + ig = _____

7. [ ] + im = _____

8. [ ] + ix = _____

in
is
it
did
big
him
rip
fix
was
of

Write the words that do not have **short i**.

9. [ ][ ]

10. [ ][ ][ ]

68

Words that are very different in meaning are called opposites. Write the word that is the opposite of the underlined word.

1. Min will <u>break</u> the toy.

2. That  door goes <u>out</u>.

3. Ben will  <u>mend</u> the paper.

4. The dog is <u>little</u>.

5. I can give the book to <u>her</u>.

in
is
it
did
big
him
rip
fix
was
of

Fill in the circle next to the word that completes each sentence.

6. She _____ a good friend.
   O is   O of

7. The boy _____ not see me.
   O was   O did

8. You can do _____.
   O in   O it

9. I have a new box _____ crayons.
   O was   O of

The dog broke the fence. How can you fix it? What tools come to mind? Write words from around the toolbox to add to the word web.

in
is
it
did
big
him
rip
fix
was
of

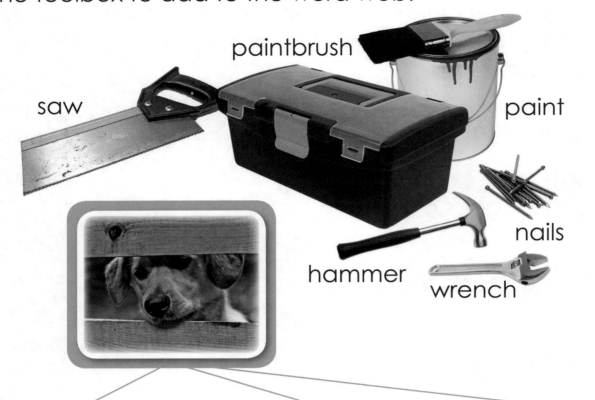

paintbrush

saw

paint

nails

hammer

wrench

_____   _____   _____
- - - - - - - - - - - - -   - - - - - - - - - - - - -   - - - - - - - - - - - - -
_____   _____   _____

Write the missing words to complete the story. Use the word web and the list.

_____
- - - - - - - - - - - -

My dog broke the fence. I will _____ it. I will get a

_____   _____
- - - - - - - - - - - -   - - - - - - - - - -

_____ to fix the fence. I will use _____ to

_____
- - - - - - - - - - - -

fix the broken part. I can also use a _____ to help

fix it. Then my dog cannot get out of the yard.

70

Name _____

Chapter 6	Chapter 7	Chapter 8	Chapter 9	Chapter 10
Short a	**Short o**	**Short e**	**Short u**	**Short i**
am	job	bed	up	in
at	God	fed	us	is
cat	mom	red	mud	it
can	hop	get	bug	did
man	top	let	fun	big
ran	got	pet	run	him
had	not	men	sun	rip
has	fox	yes	cut	fix

A vowel usually makes its _____ sound 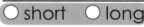 ○ short ○ long

when it is the only vowel in the word.

Sort the **short a** words by the ending sound. Write the words.

1.
_____
- - - - - - - - - - - - - - -
_____
- - - - - - - - - - - - - - -

2.
_____
- - - - - - - - - - - - - - -
_____
- - - - - - - - - - - - - - -

3.
_____
- - - - - - - - - - - - - - -
_____

4.
_____
- - - - - - - - - - - - - - -
_____

Find the words in the word search.
Circle each word. Write them.

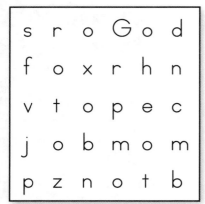

s	r	o	G	o	d
f	o	x	r	h	n
v	t	o	p	e	c
j	o	b	m	o	m
p	z	n	o	t	b

_____ _____

_____ _____

_____ _____

_____ _____

_____ _____

job
God
mom
hop
top
got
not
fox

Read each clue. Find each missing word
and write each letter in a box.

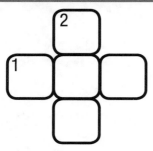

1. I have a ____ hamster.
2. I said,"____, you may
   play with my toy."

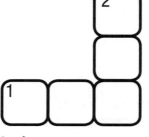

1. I sleep on my ____.
2. I ____ my dog
   a bone.

bed
fed
red
get
let
pet
men
yes

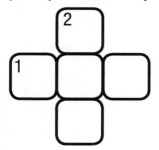

1. I like the color ____.
2. I saw two ____ ride
   the bus.

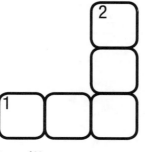

1. I will ____ my
   backpack.
2. I ____ my brother
   go first.

Name _____

Find eight **short u** words in the picture. Write them.

1.

Write each **short i** word in its matching shape.

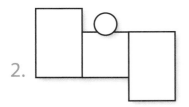

2.

3.

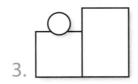

4.

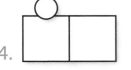

5.

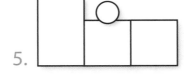

6.

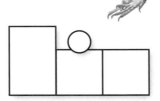

7.

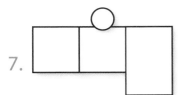

8.

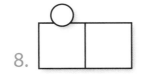

9.

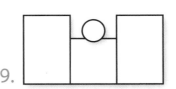

in
is
it
did
big
him
rip
fix

Listen as the teacher reads the directions.

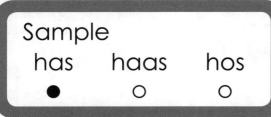

Sample
has   haas   hos
●   ○   ○

1. rin   ran   raan
    ○   ○   ○

2. Ged   gad   God
    ○   ○   ○

3. pett   pet   piit
    ○   ○   ○

4. mud   med   mot
    ○   ○   ○

5. big   bik   bek
    ○   ○   ○

6. fex   fox   foxx
    ○   ○   ○

7. am   em   om
    ○   ○   ○

8. min   men   mun
    ○   ○   ○

9. sun   san   suun
    ○   ○   ○

10. maan   mann   man
    ○   ○   ○

11. et   it   itt
    ○   ○   ○

12. gat   git   got
    ○   ○   ○

13. nat   not   nit
    ○   ○   ○

14. bugg   bogg   bug
    ○   ○   ○

15. fix   fixx   fexx
    ○   ○   ○

Name _____

12.2

Phonics
Words Ending with
Double Consonants

Pattern Words

add

puff

egg

well

will

doll

kiss

miss

Dd, **ff**, **gg**, **ll**, and **ss** are double consonants. Together they make one sound. They often follow a short vowel in a word.

Write the words that rhyme.

1.

bell

_____

2.

leg

_____

3.

sad

_____

4.

fill

_____

_____

5.

hiss

High-Frequency Words

you

live

Challenge Words

_____   _____

_____   _____

© Spelling Plus Grade 1

75

Circle each correct word. Write the word to complete each sentence.

add
puff
egg
well
will
doll
kiss
miss
you
live

1. end
   eat
   egg

   _____

   I held the _____.

2. walk
   will
   wall

   _____

   I _____ sleep.

3. mad
   sad
   add

   _____

   I can _____ to eight.

4. kiss
   pull
   gull

   _____

   I will _____ my mom.

5. mall
   doll
   fall

   _____

   I lost my _____.

6. mess
   mom
   miss

   _____

   I _____ you.

Write two words that do not end with double consonants.

7. _____

8. _____

Word Study
Words Ending with
Double Consonants

add
puff
egg
well
will
doll
kiss
miss
you
live

A sentence is a group of words that make a complete thought.

Record words and phrases.

1. | will play | | I |

_____

- -

_____ .

2. | well | | I | | will play |

_____

- -

_____ .

3. | I | | with my doll | | well | | will play |

_____

- -

_____

- -

_____ .

Draw a line to match the correct meaning of **well** to the picture word.

4. a deep water hole   •   •

5. done in a good way   •   •

Complete the story.

add
puff
egg
well
will
doll
kiss
miss
you
live

The Giant Egg

Paul found a giant _____ at the zoo.

He blew a _____ of breath to clean

the egg. The zookeeper told Paul to hide the egg

_____ in the ostrich nest. "The baby bird

will _____ inside the egg for forty days before

hatching," said the zookeeper. "Will _____

come and visit the baby ostrich?" Paul answered,

"Yes, I _____ come to visit."

78

Name

13.2

Phonics
Words Ending with ck

Pattern Words

back
neck
kick
pick
sick
rock
sock
duck

High-Frequency Words

have
or

The consonants **ck** make the /k/ sound.
They follow a short vowel in a word.

Write each word that rhymes in a shape box.

1. deck, peck

2. tack, rack

3. tick, lick

4. tuck, buck

5. dock, lock

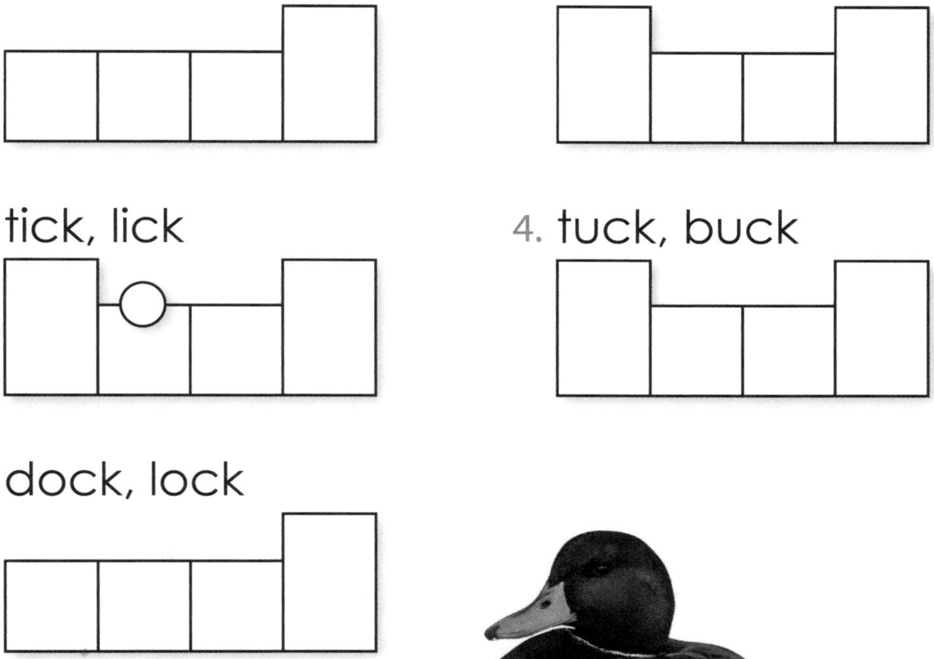

Challenge Words

Write the words to match the vowel on each
duck foot. Circle each **ck** with a black crayon.

1. o _____

2. a _____

3. u _____

4. e _____

back
neck
kick
pick
sick
rock
sock
duck
have
or

5. i _____

head

nostril

beak

neck

chest

duck

feet

Write each High-Frequency Word
in a shape box.

6. ⬚⬚⬚⬚

7. ⬚⬚

80

Word Study
Words Ending
with ck

Think about each set of words. Write the word that belongs in each set.

back
neck
kick
pick
sick
rock
sock
duck
have
or

1. foot, shoe, _____

2. punt, boot, _____

3. head, throat, _____

4. end, hind, _____

The LORD is my rock and my fortress and my deliverer.
　2 Samuel 22:2b

5. choose, gather, _____

6. swan, goose, _____

7. ill, ailing, _____

8. stone, pebble, _____

rock

Look at the duck's feet. It has skin between its toes. The duck has webbed feet.

Why did God give the duck webbed feet? Use words from the list to write about it.

_____

A _____ has webbed feet. It can use its

feet to _____ the water. Its feet help it to go

very fast. When the duck sees a fish, it puts its head

and _____ under the water. Some water may

splash on its _____. The duck's webbed feet may

help it balance on a _____. Geese and swans

_____ webbed feet, too.

back
neck
kick
pick
sick
rock
sock
duck
have
or

82

Pattern Words

end

hand

sent

went

fast

must

jump

lamp

High-Frequency Words

they

one

Write an ending to complete each word.

| st | nd | mp | nt |

1. ha_____

2. ju_____

3. se_____

4. la_____

5. e_____

6. fa_____

Say each ending and read the words.
Write a word with the same ending.

7. __ent   bent   dent   _____

8. __ust   just   rust   _____

9. __ump   lump   bump   _____

Challenge Words

_____   _____

_____   _____

Write a word that rhymes.

 mend

 stamp

1. _____

2. _____

 last

 crust

3. _____

4. _____

 bump

 band

5. _____

6. _____

end
hand
sent
went
fast
must
jump
lamp
they
one

Write the High-Frequency Words.

7. **1** _____

8. _____

Name _____

A sentence is a group of words that make a complete thought.

Order each group of words to write a sentences.

end
hand
sent
went
fast
must
jump
lamp
they
one

1. The cheetah   fast   ran

_____

- -

_____.

2. ate   A bunny   one carrot

_____

- -

_____.

3. went   into the barn   A pig

_____

- -

_____.

4. sat   The bird   on my hand

_____

- -

_____.

Use the Word Bank and the list words to write an ad in the school newspaper.

end
hand
sent
went
fast
must
jump
lamp
they
one

Word Bank
Tuesday   3:00   brand   bike

THE SCHOOL NEWS

Jump for Fun!

A _____ rope contest will

be held on _____.

Everyone is invited. Come to the

playground at _____ PM. The winner will

receive a _____ new _____.

See you there!

Pattern Words

hang

king

ring

long

sung

sink

wink

bunk

High-Frequency Words

on

but

Write the words with the same ending sound as shown on each feather.

ing

1. _____ _____

ink

2. _____ _____

ong

3. _____

ung

4. _____

ang

5. _____

unk

6. _____

Write each High-Frequency Word in a shape box.

7.

8.

Challenge Words

_____ _____

Write a word to complete each rhyme.

hang
king
ring
long
sung
sink
wink
bunk
on
but

1. Owls can blink,
   Quick as a ____.

2. When all the lights were hung,
   A Christmas song was ____.

3. A carol we sang,
   Now ornaments we ____.

4. A nightingale sang a song,
   He sang it all night ____.

5. I began to sing,
   When I found my ____.

6. A crown is what I bring,
   To a party for a ____.

The Lord is King forever and ever.
Psalm 10:16a

Name _____

Words Ending
with ng, nk

Circle the correct word that fits each meaning.

1. the ruler of the land   hang   ring   king
2. open and close one eye   wink   ring   bunk
3. has finished the song   hang   sung   on
4. a place to sleep   bunk   ring   long
5. not short   but   on   long
6. put up Christmas stockings   hang   king   ring
7. not off   wink   on   but
8. goes on your finger   long   but   ring

hang
king
ring
long
sung
sink
wink
bunk
on
but

Match the correct meaning of **sink** to the picture word.

9. to go to the bottom of the water   •   •

10. a place to wash one's hands   •   •

Match the correct meaning of **ring** to the picture word.

11. what a bell can do   •   •

12. what goes on a finger   •   •

© Spelling Plus Grade 1   89

What will sink in water? What will not sink?
Make a list. Use words from the list and the board.

Writing
Words Ending
with ng, nk

Things That Sink	Things That Do Not Sink
_____	_____
- - - - - - - - - - -	- - - - - - - - - - -
_____	_____
- - - - - - - - - - -	- - - - - - - - - - -
_____	_____
- - - - - - - - - - -	- - - - - - - - - - -

hang
king
ring
long
sung
sink
wink
bunk
on
but

duck

inner tube

ball

Write a complete sentence about something that will sink in the water. Begin with a capital letter and end with a period.

_____

- -

_____

- -

_____

Name _____

Pattern Words

ball
call
fall
hall
mall
tall
talk
walk

Use the letters on the leaves to write **all** words.

1.

_____
_____
_____
_____
_____
_____

Write two words with the **alk** ending.

2. alk _____ _____
_____ _____

High-Frequency Words

your
do

Challenge Words

_____ _____

Say the letter that begins each picture word.
Add the ending. Write the word.

1.  + all = _____

2.  + all = _____

3.  + alk = _____

4.  + all = _____

5.  + alk = _____

6.  + all = _____

ball
call
fall
hall
mall
tall
talk
walk
your
do

Write the words that do not end with **all** or **alk**.

7. _____   8. _____

Name _____

Words that are very different in meaning are called opposites. Write the word that is the opposite of the underlined word.

ball
call
fall
hall
mall
tall
talk
walk
your
do

1. A mouse is <u>short</u>.

A giraffe is _____ .

2. I can <u>run</u> to the park.

I can _____ to school.

Order the words to complete each sentence.

to   with   talk

3. Carla wanted _____ Julie.

call   a   phone

4. She made _____ .

your   have   ball

5. "Julie, I _____ ."

Circle the words that are spelled wrong.
Write each one correctly.

1. The boll hit the door.

2. I saw my friend at the mell.

3. My bag is in the hol.

4. I like to tak to my friends.

5. I col my friends on the phone.

6. Did you bring yor bike?

ball
call
fall
hall
mall
tall
talk
walk
your
do

Complete the story.

Fall

In the fall it begins to get cold. The leaves turn
_____

many colors and _____ to the ground.

They fall from _____ trees. You can go

for a _____ to see the leaves.

What will you _____ with them?

94

Chapter 12 **dd, ff, gg,** **ll, ss**	**Chapter 13** **ck**	**Chapter 14** **st, nd,** **nt, mp**	**Chapter 15** **ng, nk**	**Chapter 16** **all, alk**
add	back	end	hang	ball
puff	neck	hand	king	call
egg	kick	sent	ring	fall
well	pick	went	long	hall
will	sick	fast	sung	mall
doll	rock	must	sink	tall
kiss	sock	jump	wink	talk
miss	duck	lamp	bunk	walk

Dd, ff, gg, ll, and **ss** are double consonants. Together they make one sound. They often follow a _____ vowel in a word.

○ short   ○ long

The consonants **ck** make the /k/ sound.
They follow a _____ vowel in a word.

○ short   ○ long

Write each word in its matching shape.

1.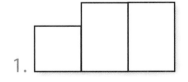

2.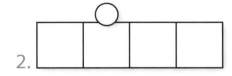

3.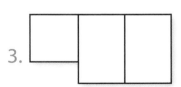

4.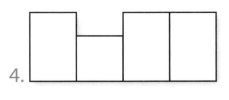

5.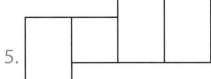

add
puff
egg
well
will
doll
kiss
miss

Sort each **ck** word by the short vowel.

1.

_____

- - - - - - - - - - - - - -

_____

2.

_____

- - - - - - - - - - - - - -

_____

3.

_____

- - - - - - - - - - - - - -

_____

4.

_____

- - - - - - - - - - - - - -

_____

_____

- - - - - - - - - - - - - -

_____

_____

- - - - - - - - - - - - - -

_____

5.

_____

- - - - - - - - - - - - - -

_____

_____

- - - - - - - - - - - - - -

_____

back
neck
kick
pick
sick
rock
sock
duck

Read each sentence. Find each missing word and write each letter in a box.

6. Ben will _____ over the puddle.
7. Tasha _____ to the store.
8. We _____ do our work.

9. The _____ train moved quickly.
10. Grandma _____ me a letter.
11. School will _____ at 3:00 PM.

end
hand
sent
went
fast
must
jump
lamp

96

Find the words in the word search. Circle each word. Write them on the lines below the puzzle.

d	j	m	b	o	s	j	k
k	e	s	u	h	i	w	y
i	l	u	n	a	n	i	r
n	o	n	k	n	k	n	i
g	n	g	d	g	q	k	n
p	g	w	h	v	t	r	g

hang
king
ring
long
sung
sink
wink
bunk

Sort each word by the ending sound.

1.

2.

ball
call
fall
hall
mall
tall
talk
walk

alk

all

_____

- - - - - - - - - - - - -

_____

- - - - - - - - - - - - -

_____

Find each word that is spelled correctly. Fill in the circle.

3. egg   agg
   o   o

4. keng   king
   o   o

5. pik   pick
   o   o

6. jump   jup
   o   o

Name _____

Pattern Words

boy

boys

box

boxes

dog

dogs

tent

tents

Plural means there is **more than one** person or thing. To make most words plural, add **s.**

Write the word for each picture.

1. _____

2. _____

3. _____

4. _____

5. _____

6. _____

If a word **ends with x**, make it plural by adding **es.**

7. _____

8. _____

High-Frequency Words

about

how

Challenge Words

_____   _____

_____   _____

Circle the ending sound for each picture word. Then write each spelling word with the same ending sound.

boy
boys
box
boxes
dog
dogs
tent
tents
about
how

1.

/s/   /z/

_____

- -

_____

2.

/s/   /z/

_____

- -

_____

- -

_____

3.

/es/   /ez/

_____

- -

_____

Write a High-Frequency Word in each sentence.

4. _____

- - - - - - - - - - - - - - - - - - -

I know _____ to count to 100.

5. _____

- - - - - - - - - - - - - - - - - - -

We will arrive in _____ an hour.

6. _____

- - - - - - - - - - - - - - - - - - -

_____ do you feel today?

Name _____

Write the words that mean **more than one**.

1. one tent _____ three _____

2. one box _____ four _____

3. one boy _____ two _____

4. one dog _____ six _____

boy
boys
box
boxes
dog
dogs
tent
tents
about
how

Write a word to complete each sentence.

5. Ten _____ go camping in the mountains.

6. Brad and Ken set up four _____.

7. One _____ fixes sandwiches for lunch.

8. Tim shares a _____ of cookies.

Look at the picture.

Writing
Plural Words
with -s, -es

boy
boys
box
boxes
dog
dogs
tent
tents
about
how

Write two or three sentences to complete the story.

Two Friends

Todd and Rex are friends. They like to camp in the woods.

The **long a** sound is heard at the beginning of **ape**.

ape

Pattern Words

ate
late
made
cake
came
name
rain
sail
day
may

A vowel followed by only one **consonant** and **silent e** usually makes its long sound.

Write the missing vowels.

1. l t

2. t

3. c k

4. n m

5. m d

6. c m

Write the **silent e** to make new words.

7. at

8. mad

Write the High-Frequency Words in the shape boxes.

9. [shape boxes]

10. [shape boxes]

High-Frequency Words

out
more

Challenge Words

When two vowels are together in a word, the first one usually makes its long sound, and the second one is silent.

ate
late
made
cake
came
name
rain
sail
day
may
out
more

Sort the **ai** and **ay** words. Write them.

1. ai

2. ay

Color spaces with **ai** words  .

Color spaces with **ay** words  .

Color spaces with **silent e** words 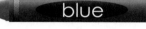 .

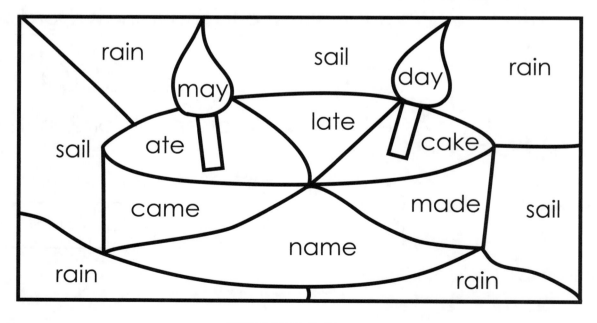

The hidden picture is a _____ .

Read the poem.

Nate's Day

The rain fell down at school all day.
I could not go outside to play.
All I could do was sit and stare
At the cold, wet world
From my small chair.

More rain fell down, so Mom came late.
She took me home; still I had to wait
For the dinner I helped her make.
And our dessert
Was chocolate cake!

ate
late
made
cake
came
name
rain
sail
day
may
out
more

Write words from the list to complete each sentence.

1. Nate could not go _____ to play.

2. The _____ made everything wet.

3. Nate's mom was not on time. She was _____.

4. Nate and his mom _____ dinner.

5. Nate _____ chocolate _____ for dessert.

Add some words of your own to the Word Bank.

Word Bank

presents
candles
ice cream

party
friends
fun

games
play
happy

ate
late
made
cake
came
name
rain
sail
day
may
out
more

Write about your birthday. Use words from the Word Bank and the list. Write complete sentences.

My Birthday

Your hands have made me and fashioned me.   Psalm 119:73a

The **long o** sound is heard at the beginning of **okapi**.

okapi

Pattern Words

go

no

so

boat

coat

rode

home

hope

old

told

High-Frequency Words

give

said

Write the words that have **old** in them.

1. _____   2. _____

When the only vowel in a word comes at the end, it usually makes its long sound.

Write the words that end with a **long o** sound.

3. [ ]   4. [ ][ ]   5. [ ][ ]

Write the High-Frequency Words.

6. _____   7. _____

Challenge Words

_____   _____

When two vowels are together in a word, the first one usually makes its long sound, and the second one is silent.

go
no
so
boat
coat
rode
home
hope
old
told
give
said

Use the letters on the sails to make **oa** words.

1.

_____

- - - - - - - - - - - - - -

_____

- - - - - - - - - - - - - -

_____

A vowel followed by only one **consonant** and **silent e** usually makes its long sound.

Add the letters. Write the word.

_____

- - - - - - - - - - - - - -

2. h + ope =

_____

- - - - - - - - - - - - - -

3. r + ode =

_____

- - - - - - - - - - - - - -

4. h + ome =

_____

My hope is in You. Psalm 39:7b

108

Use the words in the boxes to write three sentences below.

We	will go	to buy a coat.
Two boys	rode in a car	to see an old bear.
My friends	hope	to find the boat.

go
no
so
boat
coat
rode
home
hope
old
told
give
said

_____

_ _ _ _ _ _ _ _ _ _ _ _ _ _ _ _ _ _ _ _

_____

_ _ _ _ _ _ _ _ _ _ _ _ _ _ _ _ _ _ _ _

_____

_ _ _ _ _ _ _ _ _ _ _ _ _ _ _ _ _ _ _ _

_____

_ _ _ _ _ _ _ _ _ _ _ _ _ _ _ _ _ _ _ _

_____

_ _ _ _ _ _ _ _ _ _ _ _ _ _ _ _ _ _ _ _

Read the sentences and write the opposite of each underlined word.

1. I begin like [goat image]. I will stop.

_____

2. I begin like 9. The answer is yes. _____

Read the letter. Underline each misspelled word.
Write the words correctly below the letter.

Dear Grandma and Grandpa,

   I am writing hom to tell you about my trip. I rood in a baot today. The captain tald me that I was uld enough to help him steer. To keep warm, I had my new coot on. We had to go slowly soo we would not make big waves. The captain sed that I did a good job. I hap to do it again.

   Love,

   Zachary

go
no
so
boat
coat
rode
home
hope
old
told
give
said

1. _____ 2. _____ 3. _____

4. _____ 5. _____ 6. _____

7. _____ 8. _____ 9. _____

110

The **long i** sound is heard at the beginning of **ibis**.

ibis

Pattern Words

by

my

ride

bike

like

time

nine

dive

find

kind

The **long i** sound is heard when **y** is the only vowel in a word.

Write the words that end with **y**.

1.

2.

The **long i** sound is heard in **ind**.

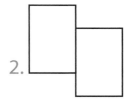

Write the words that end with **ind**.

3. _____

4. _____

Write the High-Frequency Words.

5. _____

6. _____

High-Frequency Words

them

would

Challenge Words

_____   _____

_____   _____

A vowel followed by only one **consonant** and **silent e** usually makes its long sound.

Write the missing vowels.
Then write the complete word.

by
my
ride
bike
like
time
nine
dive
find
kind
them
would

1. l k _____

2. d v _____

3. r d _____

4. t m _____

5. b k _____

6. n n _____

Write the word that begins like each picture.

7.  _____

8. _____

9. _____

10. _____

Name _____

Write the word that completes each sentence.

1. My friends are very — — — —. (kite, kind, king)

2. We — — — — to play outside. (lamp, late, like)

3. We — — — — our bikes to the lake. (ring, ride, rock)

4. I like to — — — — rocks in the lake. (find, fine, fast)

5. We also spend — — — — fishing. (tell, time, talk)

6. Once, we caught — — — — fish! (neck, nine, name)

7. We took — — — — home for dinner. (tent, told, them)

8. I have fun with — — friends. (by, be, my)

by
my
ride
bike
like
time
nine
dive
find
kind
them
would

You want to sell your bike. What other information do you need? Use the word web.

_____

cost

used   (bike)   color

_____

_____

by
my
ride
bike
like
time
nine
dive
find
kind
them
would

Write in the missing words to complete the poster. Use the word web and the list.

Bike For Sale

_____   _____

Would you _____ to buy a _____ bike?

Come _____ and take it for a _____!

It is the _____ black.

The _____ is $10.00.

Call after _____ A.M.

114

The **long e** sound is heard at the beginning of **eagle**.

eagle

> When two vowels are together in a word, the first one usually makes its long sound, and the second one is silent.

Sort the ee and ea words. Write them.

Pattern Words

be

me

we

see

seed

feel

meat

meet

weak

week

1.

ee

_____
- - - - - - - - - - -
_____
- - - - - - - - - - -
_____
- - - - - - - - - - -
_____

2.

ea

_____
- - - - - - - - - - -
_____
- - - - - - - - - - -
_____

High-Frequency Words

come

other

Challenge Words

_____   _____
- - - - - - - - -   - - - - - - - - -
_____   _____

When the only vowel in a word comes at the end, it usually makes its long sound.

Write the words that end with only one vowel.

_____   _____   _____
- - - - - - - - - - - -   - - - - - - - - - - - -   - - - - - - - - - - - -
1. _____   2. _____   3. _____

Look at the clouds to spell and write the High-Frequency Words.

_____
- - - - - - - - - - - - - - - - - -
4. _____

_____
- - - - - - - - - - - - - - - - - -
5. _____

be
me
we
see
seed
feel
meat
meet
weak
week
come
other

Write the words that rhyme with the pictures.

6.

_____
- - - - - - - - - - - -
_____
- - - - - - - - - - - -
_____

7.

_____
- - - - - - - - - - - -
_____
- - - - - - - - - - - -
_____

8.

_____
- - - - - - - - - - - -
_____

9.

_____
- - - - - - - - - - - -
_____

Sometimes words sound alike, but they are spelled in different ways and have different meanings.

Write the word that completes each sentence.

be
me
we
see
seed
feel
meat
meet
weak
week
come
other

meat   meet   weak   week

_____

1. Each _____ has seven days.

2. Mom will _____ Mrs. Pines at church.

3. The sick baby was hungry and _____.

4. I ate _____ and potatoes for dinner.

Write **me**, **we**, and **be** in ABC order.

5. _____ 6. _____ 7. _____

a b c d e f g h i j k l m n o p q r s t u v w x y z

Look at the pictures. Choose one to write about on the lines below. Use the list words and any of the words below the picture.

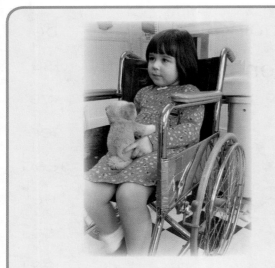

child
wheelchair
girl
help
kind

fell
book
tripped
friend
hurt

be
me
we
see
seed
feel
meat
meet
weak
week
come
other

What Would Jesus Do?

_____

- -

_____

- -

_____

- -

_____

- -

_____

Chapter 18 Plurals	**Chapter 19** Long a	**Chapter 20** Long o	**Chapter 21** Short i	**Chapter 22** Short e
boy	ate	go	by	be
boys	late	no	my	me
box	made	so	ride	we
boxes	cake	boat	bike	see
dog	came	coat	like	seed
dogs	name	rode	time	feel
tent	rain	home	nine	meat
tents	sail	hope	dive	meet
	day	old	find	weak
	may	told	kind	week

A vowel followed by only one _____ and **silent e**

○ vowel   ○ consonant

usually makes its _____ sound.

○ short   ○ long

When two vowels are together in a word, the first one usually makes its

_____ sound, and the second one is _____.

○ short   ○ long   ○ silent   ○ short

Write a word to match each picture. Use words in Lesson 18.

1. _____

2. _____

3. _____

4. _____

Find the **long a** words in the picture.
Write them on the lines.

1.

name
cake
came
ate
made
day
rain
sail
late
may

_____ _____

_____ _____

_____ _____

_____ _____

_____ _____

_____ _____

_____ _____

_____ _____

Sort the words. Write them under the correct heading.

2. ⬜ old

_____

_____

3. ⬜ o_e

_____

_____

4. ⬜ oa

_____

_____

go
no
so
boat
coat
rode
home
hope
old
told

Circle all the words with the **long i** sound found
in the word search. Write them on the lines below the puzzle.

a	o	p	b	c	n	o	z	a	p
b	n	q	a	m	m	p	l	b	o
c	m	r	b	y	l	n	i	n	e
d	l	b	z	d	k	q	k	c	n
e	r	i	d	e	j	i	e	d	m
t	k	k	y	e	i	s	y	e	l
i	j	e	m	f	h	d	i	v	e
m	i	c	k	i	n	d	x	f	k
e	h	t	w	n	g	t	w	g	j
f	g	u	v	d	f	u	v	h	n

by
my
ride
bike
like
time
nine
dive
find
kind

Read each sentence and find the missing words. Words may go across or down. Write each letter in a box.

1. Do not give the baby _____ to eat.
2. I can plant a flower _____.
3. Will you play with _____?
4. When I go to church, I can _____ new friends.

5. If you do not exercise, you will become _____.
6. When I grow up, I will _____ an airplane pilot.
7. _____ can play together.
8. There are seven days in a _____.

be
me
we
see
seed
feel
meat
meet
weak
week

Find the misspelled word in each sentence. Circle it and write it correctly.

_____

9. I stay at home if I do not feal well. _____

_____

10. Do you sae the yellow duck? _____

_____

11. Hot dogs and hamburgers are mete. _____

_____

12. My birthday is in one wekk. _____

Name _____

Short oo is heard in **book**.
Long oo is heard in **zoo**.

Pattern Words
soon
good
look
took
food
book
zoo
foot
cool
noon

Sort the words.

1. Short oo

_____

_____

_____

_____

_____

2. Long oo

_____

_____

_____

_____

_____

High-Frequency Words
many
he

Challenge Words
_____ _____

123

Write each rhyming word for the animal homes.

1. **wood**

   _____

   - - - - - - - - - - - - - - - -

   _____

2. **cocoon**

   _____

   - - - - - - - - - - - - - - -

   _____

3. **brook**

   _____

   - - - - - - - - - - - - - - -

   _____

   _____

   - - - - - - - - - - - - - - -

   _____

4. **pool**

   _____

   - - - - - - - - - - - - - - -

   _____

soon
good
look
took
food
book
zoo
foot
cool
noon
many
he

5. Color words with **short oo** orange.
   Color words with **long oo** blue.

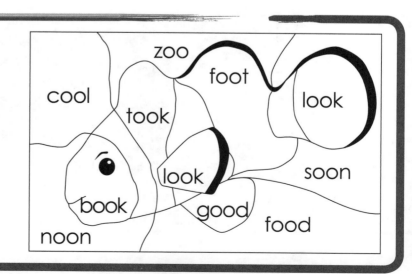

124

Name _____

Idioms are fun ways to talk about everyday things.
Use list words to complete each sentence.

1. If you are very good, you are _____ as gold.

2. If you are calm and not upset, you are as

_____

_____ as a cucumber.

3. If you said something that you wish you had not

_____

said, you put your _____ in your mouth.

4. If you do something just as you should,

_____

you do it by the _____.

5. If you have something to think about,

_____

you have _____ for thought.

6. If you are watching for something,

_____

you are on the _____ out.

Write the High-Frequency Words.

soon
good
look
took
food
book
zoo
foot
cool
noon
many
he

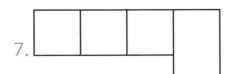

7.

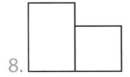

8.

Addy and her dad made a list of what they did
at the zoo. Number Addy's list in the correct order.
Write the sentences in order on the lines below.

_____ Soon it was time to go home.
_____ We took a good look at the giraffe before lunch.
_____ We ate our food at noon in the cool air.
_____ First, we got our tickets to the zoo.

Our Trip to the Zoo

soon
good
look
took
food
book
zoo
foot
cool
noon
many
he

Write the consonant blend **pl**, **bl**, **fl**, or **gl** to complete each word.

Pattern Words

play
close
blue
glad
flags
plate
class
black
fly
bless

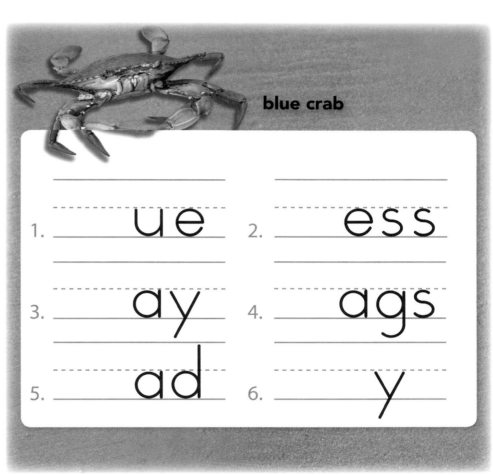

blue crab

1. _____ ue

2. _____ ess

3. _____ ay

4. _____ ags

5. _____ ad

6. _____ y

Write two words that begin like ⏰ .

7. _____

8. _____

High-Frequency Words

some
these

Challenge Words

_____

Find the word that matches each picture.
Circle it and write it on the line.

1.

bluff
blue
balloon
_____
- - - - - - - -
_____

2.

class
clean
clasp
_____
- - - - - - - -
_____

3.

plane
plate
plates
_____
- - - - - - - -
_____

play
close
blue
glad
flags
plate
class
black
fly
bless
some
these

4.

glue
glass
glad
_____
- - - - - - - -
_____

5.

flag
flags
flash
_____
- - - - - - - -
_____

6.

blast
blaze
black
_____
- - - - - - - -
_____

Write each High-Frequency Word to complete the sentence.

_____   _____
- - - - - - -   - - - - - - -

7. _____ of _____ plates are blue.

128

Name _____

Write the word that fits in each group of words.

Word Box
play
close
blue
glad
flags
plate
class
black
fly
bless
some
these

1. cup, saucer, bowl _____

2. red, yellow, green _____

3. joyful, happy, cheerful _____

4. hop, skip, run _____

5. pray, worship, praise _____

Draw a line to match each picture of **play** and **fly** with its meaning.

6. play •   • moving through the air

 7. fly •   • having a fun time

8. play •   • a small, winged insect

9. fly •   • acting out a story

Design a flag in the space below. Describe the meaning of the symbols and colors. Use list words and write complete sentences.

play
close
blue
glad
flags
plate
class
black
fly
bless
some
these

My Flag

Write the consonant blend **br**, **cr**, **fr**, or **gr** to complete each word.

Pattern Words

frame

green

brown

dry

prize

trust

dress

crops

trees

pray

1. _____ own

2. _____ ame

3. _____ ops

4. _____ een

frog

Write two words that begin like .

5. _____

6. _____

Write two words that begin like ⊱ .

7. _____

8. _____

Write two words that begin like 🥁 .

9. _____

10. _____

High-Frequency Words

from

two

Challenge Words

_____

_____

Look at each picture. Read each word and fill in the circle next to the correct word. Write the word.

1.
○ fries
○ frog
○ frame
_____

2.
○ prize
○ price
○ prince
_____

3.
○ crab
○ crops
○ cracker
_____

4.
○ grape
○ grass
○ green
_____

5.
○ press
○ pray
○ pretty
_____

6.
○ train
○ trees
○ treat
_____

7.
○ drill
○ dream
○ dress
_____

frame
green
brown
dry
prize
trust
dress
crops
trees
pray
from
two

Write the High-Frequency Words.

8. _____   9. _____

_____

Name _____

Write the correct word that completes each sentence.

_____

- - - - - - - - - - - - - - - - - - -

1. Elijah put his trust in God and said, "I will _____
   that it does not rain."

2. God told Elijah to go and live by a brook. Water from the
   _____   _____

   - - - - - - - - - - - - - - -   - - - - - - - - - - - - - - -

   brook helped the _____ stay _____ .

3. Elijah lived by the brook until it dried up. Everything
   _____   _____

   - - - - - - - - - - - - - - -   - - - - - - - - - - - - - - -

   was _____ and no _____ grew.

4. God told Elijah to leave the brook. He met a widow
   _____

   - - - - - - - - - - - - - - -

   and her son. The _____ of them were hungry.

5. Elijah asked the widow to share her food. She made
   _____

   - - - - - - - - - - - - - - -

   bread _____ flour and oil. Because she shared,
   _____

   - - - - - - - - - - - - - - -

   God allowed her jar of oil to not run _____ .

| frame |
| green |
| brown |
| dry |
| prize |
| trust |
| dress |
| crops |
| trees |
| pray |
| from |
| two |

Trust in the LORD
with all your heart.

Proverbs 3:5a

Imagine planting a strange seed. What will your seed grow into? Using the list words, complete the sentence below and describe your plant.

Today, I planted a strange seed. It grew into

_____

- -

_____

- -

_____

- -

_____

frame
green
brown
dry
prize
trust
dress
crops
trees
pray
from
two

Draw your strange plant below.

134

Name _____

Write the consonant blend **st**, **sn**, **sm**, or **sw** to complete each word.

Pattern Words

star

scat

sleep

skate

space

spell

smile

snack

swim

stop

1. _____ ar

2. _____ ack

3. _____ ile

4. _____ op

5. _____ im

Write the consonant blend **sc**, **sl**, **sk**, or **sp** to complete each word.

6. _____ eep

7. _____ ell

8. _____ at

9. _____ ace

starfish

10. _____ ate

High-Frequency Words

could

its

Challenge Words

_____ _____

_____ _____

Sort the words.

1.

Short Vowel Sounds

_____

- - - - - - - - - - - - - - - - - -

_____

- - - - - - - - - - - - - - - - - -

_____

- - - - - - - - - - - - - - - - - -

_____

- - - - - - - - - - - - - - - - - -

_____

2.

Long Vowel Sound with Vowel _ e

_____

- - - - - - - - - - - - - - - - - -

_____

- - - - - - - - - - - - - - - - - -

_____

4.

Neither Long nor Short Vowel Sound

_____

- - - - - - - - - - - - - - - - - -

_____

3.

Long Vowel Sound with Two Vowels Together

_____

- - - - - - - - - - - - - - - - - -

_____

star
scat
sleep
skate
space
spell
smile
snack
swim
stop
could
its

A question is an asking sentence.
It ends with a question mark.
Trace and write the question mark.

1. ? ? _____

star
scat
sleep
skate
space
spell
smile
snack
swim
stop
could
its

Read each asking sentence. Trace each consonant
blend and complete each word. Add a question mark.

2. Do you like to __sk_____ on ice ____

3. Can you __sp_____ that word ____

4. Did you __sm_____ at the baby ____

5. Will Mom __st_____ at the sign ____

6. Is the cat going to __sc_____ ____

7. Do astronauts fly into __sp_____ ____

8. May I __sw_____ in the pool ____

Write words from the list to complete the story.

s-l-e-e-p

star
scat
sleep
skate
space
spell
smile
snack
swim
stop
could
its

My Trip Under the Sea

_____

One night I went to _____.

_____

I had a funny dream that made me _____.

_____

I dreamed I met a sea _____ with six arms.

_____

The sea star could dance and roller _____.

_____   _____

It could _____ words while eating _____

_____

_____.

Name _____

28.2

Phonics
Digraphs sh, ch

Sh is heard in **shark** and **fish**.
Ch is heard in **child** and **beach**.

Pattern Words

wish

child

she

push

shape

check

shell

much

fish

chips

Write **ch** to complete each word. Write the word in the sentence.

1. _____ild   A _____ is here.

2. _____eck   Mom wrote a _____.

3. _____ips   Emmy ate _____.

4. mu_____   God cares so _____.

Even a child is known by his deeds.
Proverbs 20:11a

High-Frequency Words

been

now

Challenge Words

_____

_____

© *Spelling Plus Grade 1*   **139**

Write **sh** to complete each word. Write the word in the sentence.

wish
child
she
push
shape
check
shell
much
fish
chips
been
now

1. __fi__   A shark is a kind of _____.

2. __ell__   Does a clam live in a _____?

3. __pu__   Bob will _____ the swing.

4. __e__   Did _____ do her work?

5. __ape__   What _____ is a penny?

6. __wi__   Kim made a _____.

Look at the fish to spell and write the High-Frequency Words.

7. n o w

8. b e e n

Name _____

Order each group of words to write a question.
Place a question mark **?** at the end.

| to fish | | Do | | you | | like |

1. _____

| a wish | | he | | Did | | make |

2. _____

| she | | swim | | Can | | now |

3. _____

| What | | is | | shape | | the box |

4. _____

wish
child
she
push
shape
check
shell
much
fish
chips
been
now

Think of wishes. What words come to your mind?
Write them on the word web.

safety

health — (wishes) — food

wish
child
she
push
shape
check
shell
much
fish
chips
been
now

What wishes came to your mind? Write about one
wish. Use words from the word web and the list.

Draw a picture of one of your wishes.

Chapter 24 Short and Long oo	Chapter 25 L Blends	Chapter 26 R Blends	Chapter 27 S Blends	Chapter 28 Digraphs sh and ch
soon	play	frame	star	wish
good	close	green	scat	child
look	blue	brown	sleep	she
took	glad	dry	skate	push
food	flags	prize	space	shape
book	plate	trust	spell	check
zoo	class	dress	smile	shell
foot	black	crops	snack	much
cool	fly	trees	swim	fish
noon	bless	pray	stop	chips

Write the **short oo** or **long oo** words.

Short oo is heard in **book**.

1.

Long oo is heard in **zoo**.

2.

Find and circle the consonant blends with l words in the word search. Write them on the lines below.

```
c  l  a  s  s  b  t  p  r  b  m
n  b  l  u  e  v  f  l  y  q  j
p  d  f  a  k  r  c  a  m  s  s
l  g  t  c  y  j  i  y  o  a  b
a  p  g  l  a  d  r  u  c  n  l
t  d  w  o  c  y  a  t  b  r  e
e  s  s  s  p  f  d  j  u  s  s
h  w  t  e  v  b  c  t  a  l  s
n  e  m  z  b  l  a  c  k  k  u
f  l  a  g  s  o  c  v  i  r  g
```

play
close
blue
glad
flags
plate
class
black
fly
bless

Read each clue. Find each missing word and write each letter in a box.

1. The _____ frog hopped.

2. Her _____ is pink.

3. Randy won the _____.

4. The farmer picked his _____.

5. We should always _____ in God.

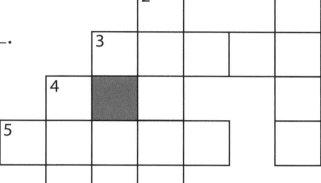

frame
green
brown
dry
prize
trust
dress
crops
trees
pray

Find the misspelled word in each sentence. Circle it and write it correctly on the line.

6. Joyce is learning to spel. _____

7. Stan went to slepp early. _____

8. In spase, it is very cold. _____

9. Mom gave us a snak to eat. _____

star
scat
sleep
skate
space
spell
smile
snack
swim
stop

Use the code to write each word.

| 1 = e | 2 = f | 3 = h | 4 = i |
| 5 = l | 6 = s | 7 = w | |

1. 6 3 1

_____

- - - - - - - - - - - - - - -

_____

2. 2 4 6 3

_____

- - - - - - - - - - - - - - -

_____

3. 7 4 6 3

_____

- - - - - - - - - - - - - - -

_____

4. 6 3 1 5 5

_____

- - - - - - - - - - - - - - -

_____

wish
child
she
push
shape
check
shell
much
fish
chips

Unscramble each word. Write it on the line.

5. k c c e h

6. s p u h

7. s h p c i

8. p a h s e

9. u m h c

10. h i d l c

146

Pattern Words

that

what

this

with

which

then

when

white

where

path

Th is heard in **that** and **sloth**.
Wh is heard in **whale**.

Write the words that begin like **the**.

Write the words that end like **sloth**.

sloth

1. _____   2. _____

3. _____

4. _____   5. _____

whale

High-Frequency Words

put

each

down

Challenge Words

_____ _____

Sort each word by its beginning or ending sound. Write the word.

1. **wh**____

_____

2. **th**____

_____

3. ____**th**

_____

that
what
this
with
which
then
when
white
where
path
put
each
down

Listen for the sounds of **th** and **wh** at the beginning or ending of each word. Write the letters.

4. ____

5. ____

6. ____

7. ____

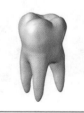

8. ____

9. ____

10. ____

11. ____

148

Look at each picture. Write a word that rhymes.

that
what
this
with
which
then
when
white
where
path
put
each
down

1. _____

2. _____

3. _____

4. _____

5. _____

6. _____

7. _____

8. _____

10

9. _____

10. _____

5th

11. _____

12. _____

The words **what**, **which**, **where**, and **when** are used in asking sentences. Write an asking word to complete each sentence.

13. _____ will you come?

14. _____ are you?

15. _____ one is mine?

16. _____ time is it?

Order the words to make a complete sentence.
Then write each sentence on a line.

1. does   Where   live?   whale   a

_____

- -

_____

- -

2. eat?   does   it   What

_____

- -

_____

3. whale   is   favorite?   your   Which

_____

- -

_____

- -

4. a   When   whale   does   breathe?

_____

- -

_____

- -

that
what
this
with
which
then
when
white
where
path
put
each
down

150

Pattern Words

Lord
start
sort
horse
far
chore
more
hard
part
jar

Or is heard in **Lord**.
Ar is heard in **jar**.

1. Write the **or** words.

porcupine

_____   _____
_____   _____
_____   _____
_____

2. Write the **ar** words.

marten

_____   _____
_____   _____
_____   _____

High-Frequency Words

an
were
his

Challenge Words

_____   _____

Complete the word web with rhyming words.

1.

fort
_____
- - - - - - - - - - - - - - -
_____

card
_____
- - - - - - - - - - - - - - -
_____

sword
_____
- - - - - - - - - - - - - - -
_____

coarse
_____
- - - - - - - - - - - - - - -
_____

(rhyming words)

cart
_____
- - - - - - - - - - - - - - -
_____

car
_____
- - - - - - - - - - - - - - -
_____

your
_____
- - - - - - - - - - - - - - -
_____
- - - - - - - - - - - - - - -
_____

Lord
start
sort
horse
far
chore
more
hard
part
jar
an
were
his

Complete each sentence with a word that rhymes with the bold word.

_____
- - - - - - - - - - - - - - -

2. The **sword** of the Spirit is the Word of the _____.

_____
- - - - - - - - - - - - - - -

3. Did you do **your** _____?

_____
- - - - - - - - - - - - - - -

4. We drove _____ in the **car**.

_____
- - - - - - - - - - - - - - -

5. _____ you sneezing because of the cat **fur**?

Help Porter Porcupine get to the branches. Use ABC order.

1.

chore

more

Lord

horse

sort

Word list:
Lord
start
sort
horse
far
chore
more
hard
part
jar
an
were
his

Write the **or** words in ABC order.

_____ _____ _____

2. _____ 3. _____ 4. _____

5. _____ 6. _____

Help Marty Marten get to the tallest tree. Use ABC order.

7.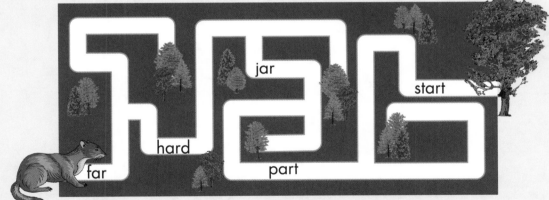

jar

start

hard

far

part

Write the **ar** words in ABC order.

_____ _____ _____

8. _____ 9. _____ 10. _____

11. _____ 12. _____

Do you have a favorite thing to collect?
Write about what you collect.

1. What do you collect?

I collect

2. Where do you get them?

I get

3. How many do you have?

I have

4. What do you keep them in?

I keep

Lord
start
sort
horse
far
chore
more
hard
part
jar
an
were
his

5. Draw a picture of your favorite thing to collect.

154

Pattern Words

hurt

verse

fern

dirt

burn

first

bird

turn

her

girl

Er, **ir**, and **ur** make the same sound. It is heard in **her**, **first**, and **turn**.

Write the missing letters to complete each word.

hermit crab

1. f __ n

2. g __ l

3. b __ d

4.  t __ n

5. v __ se

6. h __ t

7. d __ t

8. f __ st

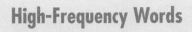

High-Frequency Words

great

again

who

Challenge Words

Sort the words.

hurt
verse
fern
dirt
burn
first
bird
turn
her
girl
great
again
who

1.

Words with **er**

_____

- - - - - - - - - - - - - - - -

_____

- - - - - - - - - - - - - - - -

_____

- - - - - - - - - - - - - - - -

_____

2.

Words with **ur**

_____

- - - - - - - - - - - - - - - -

_____

- - - - - - - - - - - - - - - -

_____

- - - - - - - - - - - - - - - -

_____

3.

Words with **ir**

_____

- - - - - - - - - - - - - - - -

_____

- - - - - - - - - - - - - - - -

_____

- - - - - - - - - - - - - - - -

_____

4.

Words that do
not have **er**, **ir**, **ur**

_____

- - - - - - - - - - - - - - - -

_____

- - - - - - - - - - - - - - - -

_____

- - - - - - - - - - - - - - - -

_____

Name _____

Put the words in order to make a complete sentence. Write each sentence.

1. verse?   was   to   Who   say   first   the

_____

- -

_____

- -

_____

2. dirt.   fern   in   planted   girl   A   her

_____

- -

_____

- -

_____

3. bird   The   its   wing.   hurt

_____

- -

_____

hurt
verse
fern
dirt
burn
first
bird
turn
her
girl
great
again
who

4. Number each set of words in ABC order.

____ burn   ____ hurt   ____ verse

____ girl   ____ fern   ____ who

____ dirt   ____ great   ____ turn

a b c d e f g h i j k l m n
o p q r s t u v w x y z

Read the poem. Circle each ir and ur word.

The Dirt

Oh, what fun I had in the dirt.
First, it got on my hands,
Then it got on my shirt,
Then in my hair,
In my eyes, on my skirt.
I scrubbed so hard that my skin hurt.
But, oh, what fun I had in the dirt!

hurt
verse
fern
dirt
burn
first
bird
turn
her
girl
great
again
who

What would you do in the dirt? Draw a picture. Then write about your picture. Begin with a capital letter and end with a period.

_____

- -

_____

- -

_____

- -

A suffix is an ending. For most words, there is no change to the base word before adding the suffix **-s**.

Pattern Words

hops

hopping

stops

stopping

hopes

hoping

makes

making

smiles

smiling

Add **s** to each base word. Write each word.

1. stop + **s** = _____

2. hop + **s** = _____

3. make + **s** = _____

4. hope + **s** = _____

5. smile + **s** = _____

wallaby

Write the High-Frequency Words in ABC order.

6. _____

7. _____

8. _____

High-Frequency Words

right

new

our

Challenge Words

_____   _____

For short vowel base words ending in one consonant, double the final consonant before adding the suffix **-ing**.

Double the final consonant and add **ing**. Write each word.

1. hop + ____ + _____ = _____

2. stop + ____ + _____ = _____

For words ending in silent **e**, drop silent **e** before adding the suffix **-ing**.

Drop the **silent e** and add **ing**. Write each word.

3. hope – e + ing = _____

4. smile – e + ing = _____

5. make – e + ing = _____

hops
hopping
stops
stopping
hopes
hoping
makes
making
smiles
smiling
right
new
our

Read the poem. Underline the rhyming words.

The Wallaby
The wallaby just hops and hops,
He seldom rests, he seldom stops.
I wish that I could go on hopping,
Seldom resting, seldom stopping.

160

Word Study
Action Words
Ending with -s, -ing

Write a word to complete each sentence.
Place the correct punctuation at the end.

hops
hopping
stops
stopping
hopes
hoping
makes
making
smiles
smiling
right
new
our

1. The wallaby _____ _____

Is the wallaby _____ _____

2. Is the man _____ _____

The man _____ _____

3. The worker _____ the traffic _____

Is the worker _____ the traffic _____

4. Is the boy _____ for a puppy _____

The boy _____ for a puppy _____

The Writing Process
1. Prewriting
2. Writing
3. Revising
4. Editing
5. Publishing

Think about someone who helped you learn this year. Complete the web using words from the list and your own words. Write a thank you note on another piece of paper.

hops
hopping
stops
stopping
hopes
hoping
makes
making
smiles
smiling
right
new
our

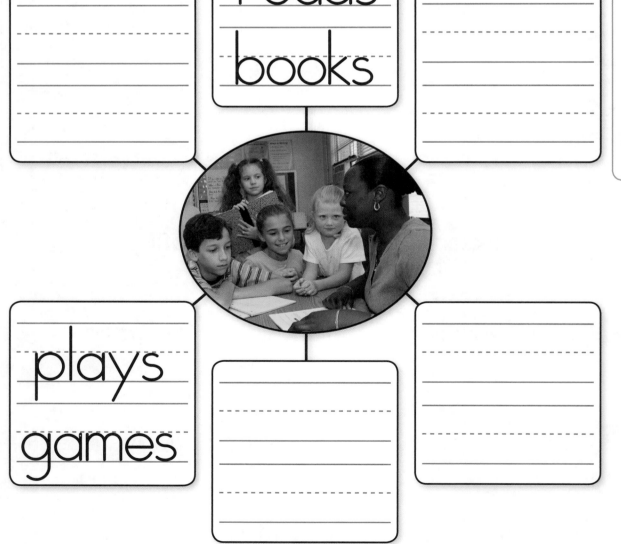

reads
books

plays
games

A suffix is an ending. For many words, there is no change to the base word before adding the suffix **-ed**.

Pattern Words

played

worked

needed

hopped

wagged

stepped

liked

hoped

ruled

skated

Add **ed** to each base word. Write each word.

1. need + _____ = _____

2. work + _____ = _____

3. play + _____ = _____

> For short vowel base words ending in one consonant, double the final consonant before adding the suffix **-ed**.

Double the final consonant and add **ed**. Write each word.

4. wag + ____ + _____ = _____

5. hop + ____ + _____ = _____

6. step + ____ + _____ = _____

High-Frequency Words

their

than

there

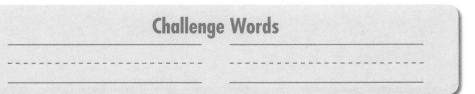

Challenge Words

_____   _____

For words ending in **silent e**, drop **silent e** before adding the suffix **-ed**.

Follow the signs to write each word.

1. skate – e + ed = _____

2. like – e + ed = _____

3. rule – e + ed = _____

4. hope – e + ed = _____

played
worked
needed
hopped
wagged
stepped
liked
hoped
ruled
skated
their
than
there

The suffix **-ed** has three sounds. Draw a line to connect each word to the correct ending sound.

5. needed •   • /ed/

6. played •   • /t/

7. liked •   • /d/

8. stepped •   • /ed/

9. ruled •   • /t/

10. skated •   • /d/

manatee

164

Read each sentence. Add **ed** to the underlined base word to tell what has happened.

1. Today, we play outside.

   _____

   Yesterday, we _____ outside.

2. Today, we skate on the ice.

   _____

   Yesterday, we _____ on the ice.

3. Today, our dogs wag their tails.

   _____

   Yesterday, our dogs _____ their tails.

played
worked
needed
hopped
wagged
stepped
liked
hoped
ruled
skated
their
than
there

Write the correct homophone in each sentence.

_____

4. _____ are some manatees.

_____

5. _____ eyes are blue or brown.

Write a High-Frequency Word in the shape box.

6.

Read the poem. Circle four ed words from your list. Underline two new ed words.

A Manatee Played with Me

When I went swimming in the sea,

A manatee came and played with me.

He wagged his flippers and seemed

to wave,

I was not scared, I was so brave.

I liked his gentle, peaceful way,

And hoped to see him another day.

played
worked
needed
hopped
wagged
stepped
liked
hoped
ruled
skated
their
than
there

Write about playing with your favorite animal. Use two ed words. Draw a picture of your animal.

Pattern Words

beehive

airplane

football

into

homework

birthday

bookmark

firefly

wildlife

rainbow

High-Frequency Words

any

number

know

A compound word is made of two smaller words.

Use the two smaller words to write a compound word.

wildlife

1.

fire + fly = _____

2.

home + work = _____

3.

wild + life = _____

4.

birth + day = _____

5.

bee + hive = _____

Challenge Words

_____ _____

Write the two words that make each compound word.

1. rainbow

_____   _____

_____ + _____

2. football

_____   _____

_____ + _____

3. into

_____   _____

_____ + _____

4. airplane

_____   _____

_____ + _____

5. bookmark

_____   _____

_____ + _____

beehive
airplane
football
into
homework
birthday
bookmark
firefly
wildlife
rainbow
any
number
know

Write High-Frequency Words to complete each sentence.

_____   _____

6. "Do you _____ your phone _____?"

_____

7. "No, I do not know _____ phone numbers."

Name _____

35.3

Word Study
Compound Words

Read each riddle. Write the answer on the line.

1. I fly above the clouds. What am I?

   _____

2. I hold your place in a book. What am I?

   _____

3. I glow in the dark. What am I?

   _____

4. I roam in the wild. What am I?

   _____

beehive
airplane
football
into
homework
birthday
bookmark
firefly
wildlife
rainbow
any
number
know

5. Number each set of words in ABC order.

____ football	____ know	____ wildlife
____ homework	____ into	____ number
____ beehive	____ birthday	____ airplane
____ any	____ rainbow	____ firefly

a b c d e f g h i
j k l m n o p q r s
t u v w x y z

A bookmark is made many different ways. It can be paper, plastic, silk, or yarn. It can have a picture, a verse, a poem, or some other words on it. How would you design a bookmark? Design one below.

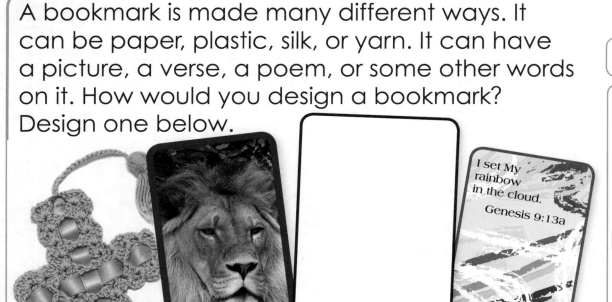

I set My rainbow in the cloud.
Genesis 9:13a

beehive
airplane
football
into
homework
birthday
bookmark
firefly
wildlife
rainbow
any
number
know

A bookmark is very useful. It marks a person's place in a book. Write about the bookmark you have designed.

Chapter 30
Digraphs th, wh
that
what
this
with
which
then
when
white
where
path

Chapter 31
Words with or, ar
Lord
start
sort
horse
far
chore
more
hard
part
jar

Chapter 32
Words with er, ir, ur
hurt
verse
fern
dirt
burn
first
bird
turn
her
girl

Lesson 33
Action Words
Ending with -s, -ing
hops
hopping
stops
stopping
hopes
hoping
makes
making
smiles
smiling

Lesson 34
Action Words
Ending with -ed
played
worked
needed
hopped
wagged
stepped
liked
hoped
ruled
skated

Lesson 35
Compound
Words
beehive
airplane
football
into
homework
birthday
bookmark
firefly
wildlife
rainbow

Read Chapter 30 words. Use your crayons to follow the directions below.

1. Circle the words that begin with **th**  red .

2. Circle the words that end with **th** blue .

3. Circle the words that begin with **wh**  green .

Read each sentence and find the missing word.
Write each letter of the word in a box.
Words may go across or down.

1. Making my bed is a ____.

2. I want some ____.

3. Jesus is ____.

4. You can ride on a ____.

5. The car would not ____.

6. I had a ____ in the play.

Lord
start
sort
horse
far
chore
more
hard
part
jar

Find the **er**, **ir**, and **ur** words in the picture. Write them on the lines.

7.

her
girl
dirt
hurt
burn
first
turn
verse
bird
fern

Name _____

Find the hidden list words. Circle them.

o	p	s	n	a	l	h	o	p	s	o	s
e	s	t	o	p	s	p	y	v	x	h	m
c	z	o	o	v	o	s	n	c	w	o	i
t	v	p	h	o	p	p	i	n	g	p	l
h	c	p	x	m	a	k	e	s	c	i	i
o	s	i	c	v	r	m	a	m	c	n	n
p	a	n	x	a	d	o	m	i	x	g	g
e	c	g	h	o	p	i	k	l	z	q	o
s	o	e	e	r	v	g	r	e	r	s	v
m	a	k	i	n	g	x	o	s	b	w	n

hops
hopping
stops
stopping
hopes
hoping
makes
making
smiles
smiling

Connect the dots next to the words spelled correctly.

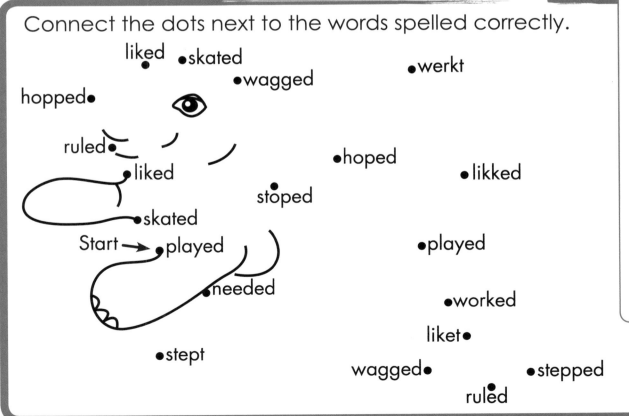

liked   •skated
       •wagged   •werkt
•skated

hopped•

ruled•
   •liked   •hoped   • likked
       •skated   •stoped

Start→ •played   •played
       •needed

       •worked
                    liket•
•stept
       wagged•   •stepped
              ruled•

played
worked
needed
hopped
wagged
stepped
liked
hoped
ruled
skated

Use a word from each column to write a compound word. Cross each word off the list as it is used.

book	bee	in	bow
air	fire	wild	hive
		foot	plane
		rain	ball
		to	fly
		life	mark

beehive
airplane
football
into
homework
birthday
bookmark
firefly
wildlife
rainbow

Name _____

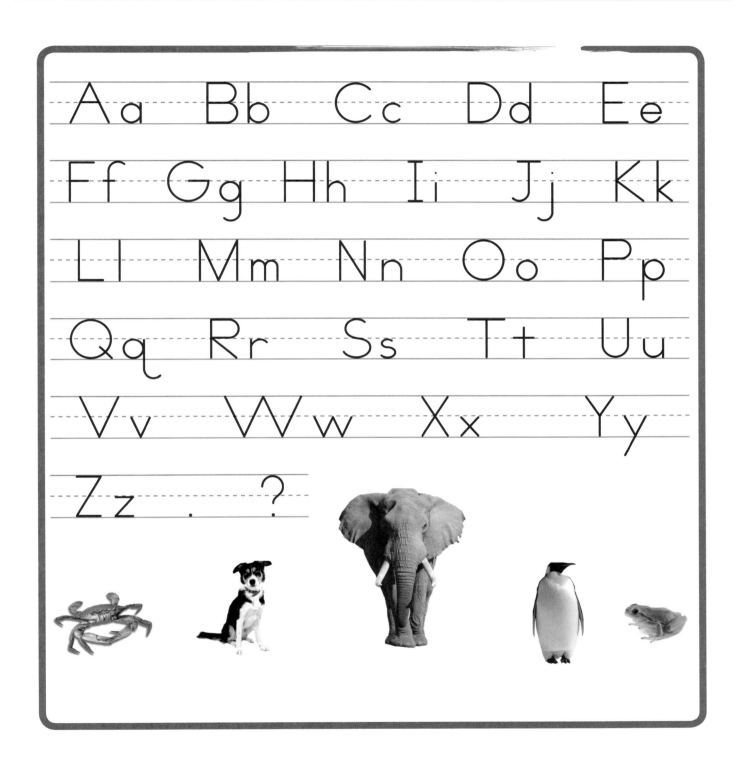

Aa Bb Cc Dd Ee
Ff Gg Hh Ii Jj Kk
Ll Mm Nn Oo Pp
Qq Rr Ss Tt Uu
Vv Ww Xx Yy
Zz . ?

Name

A

a	am	as
about	an	at
add	and	ate
again	any	
airplane	are	

B

back	bike	book	bug
ball	bird	bookmark	bunk
be	birthday	box	burn
bed	black	boxes	but
beehive	bless	boy	by
been	blue	boys	
big	boat	brown	

C

cake	check	close	crops
call	child	coat	cut
came	chips	come	
can	chore	cool	
cat	class	could	

D

day	dive	dogs	dry
did	do	doll	duck
dirt	dog	down	

E

each
egg
end

F

fall	find	fly	frame
far	firefly	food	from
fast	first	foot	fun
fed	fish	football	
feel	fix	for	
fern	flags	fox	

G

get   go   great
girl   God   green
give   good
glad   got

_____ _____ _____

_____ _____ _____

_____ _____ _____

_____ _____ _____

H

had	have	homework	hopped
hall	he	hop	hopping
hand	her	hope	hops
hang	him	hoped	horse
hard	his	hopes	how
has	home	hoping	hurt

_____ _____ _____

_____ _____ _____

_____ _____ _____

_____ _____ _____

I

I   into   it

in   is   its

J

jar

job

jump

K

kick   king   know

kind   kiss

L

lamp	like	long
late	liked	look
let	live	Lord

M

made	many	men	mud
makes	may	miss	must
making	me	mom	my
mall	meat	more	
man	meet	much	

N

name	new	noon	number
neck	nine	not	
needed	no	now	

_____

_____

_____

_____

O

of	one	our
old	or	out
on	other	

_____

_____

_____

_____

P

part	pick	played	puff
path	plate	pray	push
pet	play	prize	put

_____

Q

_____

R

rain	red	ring	rode
rainbow	ride	rip	ruled
ran	right	rock	run

_____

S

said	sink	some	stops
sail	skate	soon	sun
scat	skated	sort	sung
see	sleep	space	swim
seed	smile	spell	
sent	smiles	star	
shape	smiling	start	
she	snack	stepped	
shell	so	stop	
sick	sock	stopping	

T

talk	the	they	top
tall	their	this	trees
tent	them	time	trust
tents	then	to	turn
than	there	told	two
that	these	took	

U

up
us

V

verse

W

wagged	well	which	wish
walk	went	white	with
was	were	who	words
we	what	wildlife	worked
weak	when	will	would
week	where	wink	

_____ _____ _____

- -

_____ _____ _____

- -

_____ _____ _____

X

_____ _____ _____

- -

_____ _____ _____

- -

_____ _____ _____

Y

yes
you
your

Z

zoo